How Golf Clubs Really Work

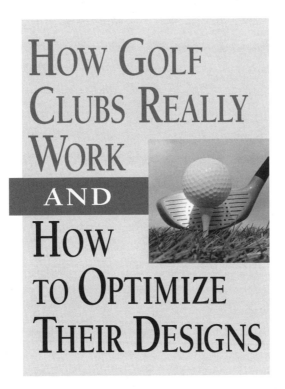

AND

How to Optimize Their Designs

BY FRANK D. WERNER
AND RICHARD C. GREIG

with ROGER P. GANEM

Published by Origin Inc, 3975 So. Hwy. 89, Jackson, WY 83001

Distributed by Tech Line Corp, 3975 So. Hwy. 89, Jackson, WY 83001

First Edition

Chapter lead-ins and Chapter 1 by Roger P. Ganem
Book design by Julie McIntyre
Editing by Peter and Jeanne Anderson

Printed in the United States of America

Publisher's Cataloging-in-Publication Data
(Provided by Quality Books, Inc.)

Werner, Frank D.
    How golf clubs really work and how to optimize their
designs / by Frank D. Werner and Richard C. Greig. -- 1st ed.
    p. cm.
Includes bibliographical references and index.
LCCN: 99-97823
ISBN: 0-9677625-0-2

    1. Golf clubs (Sporting goods)   I. Greig,
Richard C. II. Title.

GV976.W47 2000   796.352'028
           QBI00-181

WARNING-DISCLAIMER

Each chapter has a general section for the serious golfer and most have Technical Notes giving scientific back-up material and extensive data of interest to designers and researchers. This book may be read from the beginning, but most chapters are readable independently.

TABLE OF CONTENTS

LIST OF FIGURES

LIST OF TABLES

PREFACE

Much of this book was adapted from some 70 articles which we have written for monthly publication in Japan, starting in 1995, in *Golf Equipment World*, Tokyo. They were translated into the Japanese language by the international editor, Mr. Mitsumasa Katayama. Our early research on drivers was stimulated by the interest and cooperation of Mr. Tomoyuki Tawarada and his firm, J. Osawa & Company of Tokyo. We are grateful to Mr. Mitsumasa and Mr. Tawarada. We are also indebted to the many golfers who participated in our various tests.

We especially thank Roger P. Ganem. He has been our good friend and advisor in numerous areas of mutual interest. As an experienced golf writer, he wrote Chapter 1 with the perspective of golfers in mind. He also suggested and wrote the lead-in sentences following the title of each of the other chapters.

Roger is a graduate of Boston University's first School of Public Relations. He combined journalism and golf as a career. He was an executive at A. G. Spalding in promotion and advertising and later was Instruction-Technical Editor at *Golf Magazine*. He was affiliated with the USGA in New York City in the Joe Dey, P. J. Boatwright, Frank Hannigan, and Robert Sommers years. Later, he became executive director of the Florida Section of PGA and its South Florida Section when it was divided. He is author of 3 golf books and has been ghost writer for many tour professionals. We are lucky to have his help.

We felt that it was appropriate to refer to our club designs in a few instances to illustrate results. Tech Line Corp has rights to our patents issued and pending on some of the material presented here.

"Grafalloy" and "Attack Lite" are trademarks of True Temper Sports; "Tech-Line" and "BIGFACE" are trademarks of Tech Line Corp.

ABOUT THE SPECIAL SYMBOLS AND TERMS

Many variables are referred to by 3, 2, or 1 letter symbols. Most such symbols are defined at the beginning of each chapter where they are used. Consistent with these, is a complete set of definitions found in the Appendix. A few definitions have infrequent use and are defined only in the Technical Notes where they appear. This system of giving definitions causes some repetition, but should add to your convenience, and minimizes uncertainty. In many cases, the exact meanings are important and the definitions are essential.

Many definitions are "standard deviations" which is a statistics term, the basis of the bell-shaped curve, showing the variability (errors) of the item in question. For example, on a 10 foot putt, the green itself causes errors of distance even with perfect putts and the standard deviation of distance is 2.4 inches (2%). This means that 68.3% of stop points would be between one standard deviation too short and one standard deviation too long when there are no other errors (as if they were all perfect putts). Thus, the remaining putts (31.7%) would fall outside this band of plus or minus 2.4 inches (4.8 inches total). Symbols for standard deviation terms all start with the lower case letter "d".

We don't use terms common in advertising such as "a low boring shot" (it is merely a low shot, there is no boring effect, and a low loft angle and other things will cause it); "get the ball up" or "get the ball airborne" (high loft angle and other things will do that); or "MOI" in place of moment of inertia, or "torque" for torsional stiffness of a shaft (torque has a very different technical meaning.) .

COMMENTS, SUGGESTIONS AND CORRECTIONS

We will appreciate your thoughtful ideas for a future edition of this book. Particularly valuable are errors which you may find, passages which are hard to understand, subjects which should be discussed more fully, and similar improvements.

We will use such material and will cite your name as "personal communication" for the most significant suggestions, unless you request otherwise. There will be no other compensation to you unless mutually agreed in advance in writing.

Such communications may be submitted to Tech Line's web page at www.techlinegolf.com or by mail to Tech Line at 3975 S. Hwy 89, Jackson, WY 83001 or the publisher (Origin Inc) at the same address.

Part One

OUR MODEL OF A GOLF HIT

WHY SHOULD YOU READ THIS BOOK?

by ROGER P. GANEM

IT HIGHLIGHTS INSIGHTS ABOUT OVERSIGHTS AND ALL GOLFERS SHOULD EXERCISE THEIR RIGHTS.

Have you ever borrowed a friend's club and hit a sensational shot, making you wonder what is wrong with yours? A Ph.D. and a near-Ph.D. in aerospace engineering have dedicated themselves and more than a decade of experimental research and design of golf clubs. They are now offering to you their intriguing analysis based on fundamental physics and mathematics, as well as their extensive and amazing new kinds of tests. You will be able to read, perhaps for the very first time, about the whys and wherefores of the flight of the ball and how to maneuver it, as well as the definitive part your clubs play in this often frustrating but fascinating sport.

You will also become more enlightened about the real importance of face curvature (bulge and roll) and whether your driver is ideal for you... *AND* what is the best club length, head weight and loft angle for maximum distance... *AND* why the face surfaces of irons are *not* curved... *AND* correct head design will not only keep the ball in play, but also add precious distance... *AND* the scatter of your stop points (hit more fairways and greens).

How Golf Clubs Really Work and How to Optimize Their Designs – while highly technical and scientific, contains the answers to many of the problems that the sport of golf often throws our way.

Dr. Frank Werner and Richard Greig of Tech Line have gone to great lengths to de-mystify the factors that play a part in your efforts, whether you are the gifted professional, a golf instructor or the beleaguered amateur, male or female.

Much of this information has never been published, and much is unknown to most of us. The extensive "Technical Notes" at the end of most chapters will be of much interest to club designers, researchers and golfers with some scientific background. Their findings are consistent with the expe-

rience of golfers and their studies and conclusions qualitatively confirm their research.

This book also discusses Tech Line's research on the mechanical properties of the ground over which the game is played (the grass on greens, fairways and tees); their experimental laboratory research; and specific results of explorations of the effects of variables such as golfer characteristics, design variables, wind, temperature, humidity, altitude, elevation or depression of the landing area, the statistical combination of errors, and more.

The book is not intended as a guidebook for the design of clubs, but as an introduction to the fundamentals of how golf club design may be optimized for best performance. The reader will be hypnotized, especially with the abbreviations. Some will prefer to use this book as a reference, educating themselves so as to increase their enjoyment of the game, rather than completely reading all parts.

The serious golfer will find useful information about the behavior of shots under various conditions, confirming information he may already know, and also entirely new information.

The book is also not intended for promotional purposes, but in a few instances some of Tech Line's own patented designs have been used to illustrate results. On the next page are some of the common situations contained in the book.

You will be pleased to know that Werner and Greig are much better at engineering than at golf. (They work too hard and too long to have low handicaps.)

This book will lead to much new thinking about golf. It is different from any book you have ever read about golf, in format, style, and content, as you will see in all the other chapters.

Now, read on for enlightening and incredible

discoveries and conclusions by two dedicated scientists of the tools of your business or favorite pastime – GOLF.

Here are some of the common topics contained in this book.

1.   *Characteristics of the scatter of hits on the faces of clubs and those partly off the face.*

2.   *Factors that affect distance.*

3.   *Full and partial shots with irons.*

4.   *Effects of moving the ball back in the stance.*

5.   *Greens that are above or below the golfer.*

6.   *Estimating wind velocity and its effects.*

7.   *Errors due to hits which are too low or too high on the face.*

8.   *Advice for best aiming.*

9.   *Suggestions for causing or avoiding hooks and slices.*

10. *Undetected scuffing with the putter.*

11. *How far past the hole one should putt.*

12. *A discussion of unnecessary putting errors.*

Here are some of the abbreviations. Do not fear, you will not be tested.

AA   *Angle between the target direction and the intersection of the swing plane and ground planes.*

CA   *Contact angle.*

LA   *Loft angle.*

LIA *Lie angle.*

MD   *Maximum distance.*

ZBR *Bounce and roll distance for clubs other than putters, measured from where the ball hits down and the flight (carry) ends.*

WA   *Angle which describes rotations of the club around a line connecting the grip, butt and the head cg (center of gravity), zero when the face is square to target.*

HS   *Head speed.*

dAA, dHS and dWA errors *Stroboscopic photos in dim light of swing of numerous golfers hitting balls. (The clubs and golfers had reflecting tape so Werner and Greig could make accurate measurements of the positions.)*

POF *Hits which are partly off the face.*

OUR TECHNICAL MODEL

A GENERAL DESCRIPTION OF HOW WE ANALYZED GOLF CLUBS AND GOLF SHOTS WITH ALLOWANCE FOR GOLFER VARIATIONS, WEATHER, ETC. YOU MAY HAVE FIGURED OUT SOME OF THESE YOURSELF.

USES OF MODELS

In the technical world of physics and engineering, scale models of ships and many other things are considered as "physical" models. Another kind of model, the one we will use here, is a mathematical model based on the physics and engineering which describes the real system and allows us to change inputs and find out what happens to the outputs. Both mathematical and physical models are widely used in other sciences such as entirely different physical processes, chemical processes, economics, etc.

Models are powerful tools for many purposes and often there is no substitute in sight other than ignoring the fundamentals and hoping for the best. Fortunately most things in life do not require that you have much concern with models. You can drive a car, for example, with great confidence that good experience is adequate and if you are skilled, you can very reasonably hope for the best.

Golf, too, works well without models, but good models are very helpful for optimum designing of clubs and for understanding and getting the most out of them.

In our application, the equations describing the model are programmed into a computer, which is advantageous because it allows changes in inputs of design and of golfer variables and quickly shows what happens to the golf shot.

Using a computer allows study of both minute changes and large changes of one or more variables when all others are held precisely constant. This is usually impossible or impractical for testing with a physical model (actual golfers) because of the difficulty of changing only one variable with no changes or negligible changes in any of the numerous other variables.

Further, testing requires endless changes in the test equipment and always includes unwanted experimental errors. Specific advantages of modeling are detailed in some of the following chapters.

MISUSE OF MODELS

A model may have severe limitations if its description of the process is poor or erroneous, or if erroneous inputs are used. Such faults create difficult problems in models of many physical processes such as weather, and in models in the social sciences; and they often lead to erroneous claims and conclusions. Careful modeling and careful use of the model are essential, coupled with tests to make sure the model agrees with reality.

In some fields modeling has a bad name because of poor design of the model, faulty or even dishonest inputs, and careless reporting which is incomplete or misleading. Similar things can be said about the uses of statistics. We have tried hard to avoid these shortcomings.

A basic way to learn if the model and its use are reasonable is to compare results of mathematical tests

SYMBOLS AND DEFINITIONS	
AA [deg] alignment angle, the angle between the path of the clubhead at impact and the target direction, positive toward the left.*	**HS** [mph] head speed, speed of the cg of the head just prior to impact.
	HW [gm] head weight (mass), weight of the head without shaft.
cg [ ] center of gravity (more precisely center of mass); its location is usually given in inches.	**LA** [deg] loft angle.*
	MD [yd] maximum distance, the value of CHD with a specific shaft and grip and with specific values of HW, CLG, and HS, with no golfer errors and when the head design is optimized for this condition.
CHD [yd] center hit distance (more precisely the distance of a hit at the face center with no golfer errors, including the flight (carry), bounce and roll, for our reference ball under reference atmospheric conditions, on a representative level fairway).	
	ZBR [yd] bounce and roll distance for clubs other than putters, measured from where the ball hits down and the flight (carry) ends.
CLG [in] club length.*	
HCP [ ] handicap.	*More detail will be found for these items in the Appendix.*

using the model with results of actual tests, in this case, using golfers and various golf clubs. We have done many such comparisons on a quantitative basis, and we are confident of good accuracy of most results described in this book. In a few cases, the model provides only an approximate indication of trends, and this is much better than no knowledge at all.

Our Model

Our model allows us to study the flight (carry) and bounce and roll distance (ZBR) of golf shots with drivers, fairway woods, irons, and putters. It allows us to show the effects of changes in wind, air temperature, altitude, humidity, elevation or depression of the landing area, design changes in the golf club, changes of HS, and results of the main errors made by golfers.

It is especially important that when used properly, the model allows us to find the optimum combination of club design variables.

Use of our model required making measurements on actual golfers for numerical (quantized) values of such things as scatter (which we express as standard deviation) of hits on the club face, variations in HS, variations of AA and variations of clubhead angular position at impact. Our measurements showed how these things depend on HCP. We also had to study characteristics of the turf and how ZBR varies with speed, direction of travel, and spin of the ball.

For drivers, we needed to know the optimum combination of CLG and HW to use as inputs to our computer model. This is required to assure maximum CHD. No organized study of this problem has been published. Details of how we studied the swings of golfers to find optimum CLG and HW are discussed in the Technical Notes.

Golfers think of distance of drives in yards and of putts in feet, but they miss putts by inches and shaft length is in inches. They may think of head weight (properly called mass) in ounces or grams; time in seconds or hours; and angles in degrees, not radians. We chose to use golfers' familiar units and as a result, our dimensions are not standardized and consistent. This is no problem for computers, but technical readers must take note of the units.

We will often indicate the units of measure as abbreviations inside square brackets such as [in],

meaning inches. Some variables are dimensionless (independent of dimensions) and are indicated as [ ]. An example is the ratio of the weight of the ball to the weight of the head, which would be ounces divided by ounces or grams divided by grams; the ratio has the same value in either case and is not dependent on the units. Mostly, we use deg for degrees, in for inches, ft for feet, yd for yards, mph for miles per hour, sec for seconds, lb for pounds of mass, lbf for pounds of force, gm for grams, rpm for revolutions per minute, and rps for revolutions per second.

Figure 2-1 illustrates the coordinate system which we call the "head frame" (these coordinates are as if attached to the head, going along wherever the head might be moved.) The positive directions of the X, Y, and Z coordinates are indicated in the figure. The coordinates of the center of gravity (cg) location are given as examples. A similar scheme is used for the fairway frame. We use many other frames of reference which are unnecessary details here.

Please notice that we will describe effects for right-handed golfers. Left-handed golfers will experience opposite effects.

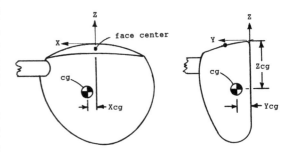

Fig. 2-1 *Definition of Xcg, Ycg, and Zcg. As shown, Xcg and Ycg are positive and Zcg is negative. The head frame coordinate axes X, Y, and Z are also shown.*

Moment of Inertia

Golfers often see discussions of "moment of inertia" which many golf writers abbreviate as MOI. Various examples are given, commonly a spinning figure skater who extends her arms or pulls them in close to her body. This gives a feeling for moment of inertia, but in technical language, it illustrates conservation of angular momentum, not moment of inertia directly. Moment of inertia is a measure of how easy or how difficult it may be to change the speed of rotation of a body about an axis of rotation. Moment of inertia about one axis gives an incomplete description of the inertia of a club head; 6 terms are required for a complete description.

You may get a better understanding of moment of inertia from a different example. Consider a very small top and a very large top (or even a large flywheel.) It takes only a small effort to change the speed of the small top or to bring it up to a desired speed. It takes a much larger effort to do this to the large top. Of course, the reason is that the large top has much larger moment of inertia about the vertical axis than the small one. This is why an off-center hit toward the toe or heel on a small driver head will turn it around a vertical axis much more than the same off-center hit on a large driver head. Moments of inertia about other axes also affect off-center hits.

TECHNICAL NOTES

The status of golf club modeling

References 4, 5, 6, and 7 discuss mathematical modeling of some of the important relations of golf clubs, their design, and their use. In all cases, the research reported in the references deals in depth with only one model with few or no sub-models, and we have found no attention to connecting all such research together to provide a general model such as we discuss in this book.

Even such ball-club impact modeling as has been published is limited to specific features of the impact and does not provide inputs for the dozens of variables needed for a good definition of an actual club in actual use.

Many of these references are valuable to anyone working with this problem. It happened that we started our research before most of the references were published and we have used mainly References 1, 2, and 7 and a few parts of the other references as noted. In those cases our work is very similar. Some of the references concentrate on modeling the swing. We did little of this. Instead, we concentrated on the impact. We represent variations in a golfer's swing at impact by what we call golfer errors. We can vary a number of inputs to simulate effects of various kinds of swings and skill levels.

The model

The heart of our model is the mathematical description of the impact of clubhead and ball, ensuing flight, and ZBR. The impact modeled is the general, non-collinear case. We treated the head as a rigid body which is a close approxima-

tion. Impacts may be anywhere on the face so we designed the model to cope properly with a description of the face surface shape.

We studied shaft bending dynamics and concluded that we should include 2 to 3 inches of the shaft tip as if it were a rigid part of the head, slightly increasing the head's mass and mass distribution terms. We disregarded the upper part of the shaft during the half millisecond or so of impact. Shaft stiffness is too low and impact time is too short for the upper part of the shaft to participate in the dynamics of impact.

The impact of club and ball meets the usual conditions for an ideal impact. Thus, our impact analysis needs only the normal and shear coefficients of restitution and we need not examine the force-time details during the impact, with the exception described in the following paragraph.

We used a modification to the ideal impact for estimating an adjustment to the direction of launch of the ball. The ideal impact provides an instantaneous change in angular velocity with no angular displacement during the impact. For a finite duration of impact, we approximated the impact force as a .0005 second half sine wave, and that allowed calculation of the rotation angle vs. time. We calculated the temporal mean of this rotation angle and used it to adjust the initial flight direction. This was always small and we believe it is not an important factor in the model.

We used a ball which was well known a few years ago (the "reference ball") and measured its normal coefficient of restitution. We used published values for shear coefficient of restitution, weight, size, moment of inertia, and aerodynamic coefficients as further detailed in Chapter 26. That chapter also gives guidance to use of other balls.

The model includes various sub-models. We used numerical integration of the aerodynamics of ball flight to provide an accurate description of the flight portion of a golf shot. We modeled ZBR with empirical equations, fitted by least squares, which approximate our tests on fairways and greens. We derived a sub-model which shows effects of HW and CLG on HS which, with the central model, yield CHD.

For the ZBR equations, we designed and built a ball launcher able to project balls downward with controllable speed, direction, backspin, and side spin. It used 2 small pneumatic tires spinning at adjustable, different rates, spaced apart a little less than one ball diameter. For a launch, the ball was introduced between these spinning tires and ejected out the other side. We used it to make many measurements of bounce and roll after a shot lands on the fairway as a function of landing angle, landing speed, and spin rate. We found that side spin had little effect on ZBR.

We used various separate programs with inputs to define the head geometry and distribution of its material. These programs have outputs of mass, all 6 inertia terms, and 3 cg location terms as required inputs for the impact model.

Chapter 4 describes tests which we made with many golfers to evaluate standard deviations of the scatter of hits on the face of the driver (the hit pattern), of angular orientation of the head at impact, of HS, and of AA.

The model includes inputs which allowed us to study scatter of stop points of hits in the presence of any one or any combination of as many as 5 golfer errors. It is provided with algorithms to iterate automatically on various design variables (meaning to repeat many times with progressively better values until the output is as near as possible to the desired result) to minimize scatter of stop points and maximize distance, allowing us to find optimum values.

Many of the multiple equations used were nonlinear and some were differential and integral equations. Usually, we used the so-called Simplex method to find solutions by iteration. The Simplex method is described in various textbooks on linear programming. In a few situations, we iterated manually.

Optimum CLG and HW for
maximum CHD, an example of the model's use

As inputs for our model, we needed to know the CLG and HW combination which gives maximum CHD. We have heard various ideas about CLG and HW. Golf club designers are tending to lengthen shafts, but there remains the question of what CLG and HW is best. The United States Golf Association once displayed a driver with CLG over 72 inches; some tour professionals have experimented with CLG up to 60 inches. The best combination of these 2 variables (CLG and HW) has not previously been identified, and to make it more complicated, a change in CLG also affects optimum location of the cg of the head and LA.

Without modeling, it is nearly impossible to make tests and obtain good decisions because with each CLG, it is necessary to try several HW values, and for each value, the cg of the head and the LA need to be changed to properly suit the golfer making the experiment.

We think golf club designers have done remarkably well at solving this problem, considering the difficulties, but better ways to optimize CLG and HW make a significant improvement.

We used a special procedure of testing with 9 different clubs (combinations of 3 CLG and 3 HW values) and many golfers, and measured head speed. The model determined MD for each swing as if it were a perfect center hit with LA

and cg location optimized for the head speed. We then fitted curves to the data and from this we found the optimum CLG-HW combination. This process greatly reduced testing problems by use of the model to find MD for each hit.

More details of testing, data reduction, and conclusions about club length are discussed in Chapter 20.

Our bounce and roll models (ZBR)
for fairways and greens

The golf ball launcher described above could be adjusted to aim in any direction – up, level, or down – with adjustable velocity, backspin, and side spin. We aimed it downward on a good, representative fairway and measured ZBR for many different settings which were representative of golf shots.

We selected a reasonable form for the equation below and found its coefficients by least squares. We used it in our model for fairways.

$$ZBR = (.868*V + .00173*V^2) * \cos(k + 24.4 + .00112*N)$$
[yd], where
V is the velocity of impact with the ground [ft/sec],
k is the angle of impact above horizontal [deg], and
N is the backspin rate (always negative) [rpm].

Greens are usually the target for irons and the shorter woods. Balls which land on the green have different ZBR from balls which land on the fairway. Again, we selected a reasonable form for the equation below and found its coefficients by least squares.

$$ZBR = c1*Vh + c2*Vh^2 + c3*A*Vv \text{ [yd], where}$$
Vh is the horizontal component of impact speed [mph],
Vv is the vertical component of impact speed [mph], and
A is spin rate of the ball (– for backspin) [rpm].
c1 = .0644,
c2 = +.01300, and
c3 = +.0000217.

For putting, we used a 3rd ZBR equation which is given as distance of the putt (PD) in Chapter 30.

Design procedure

We first chose a golfer by his HCP and HS, then the shaft and CLG, then the HW which maximizes CHD, often modifying HW for practical reasons such as head strength. Next we operated the program to optimize head design variables for maximum CHD, then used it to optimize face surface shape to minimize scatter of stop points. These steps normally need to be repeated many times because desirable input changes appear as the process proceeds. Much of this process is manual iteration. In principle, with much complication, it could be done automatically in the program as with most of our iterations. Our model also provides a great variety of various interesting and useful outputs such as trajectories, launch conditions, landing conditions, height and numerous other items.

The future of golf modeling

An interesting possibility would be to model the entire golf game so as to give a representative score for 18 typical holes. Such a model would include main golfer errors and each club's physical characteristics on each shot, starting at the first hole with the driver. On shots where maximum distance is not needed, the appropriate club would be selected automatically. The process would continue until the last putt is holed out, then the other holes would be modeled similarly. Some arbitrary inputs would be necessary as an adjustment for such things as shots into hazards or the rough.

We have modeled putts to hole out, and have given thought to rating irons intended to hit the green in terms of remaining hits to hole out.

To model the entire game for a typical course is daunting, but seems feasible and interesting. If done, it could provide a particularly meaningful rating factor for golfers to show realistically how much improvement in their score to expect for a change of any or all clubs. As such, it seems to be the ultimate rating.

Various refinements would be desirable for the modeling we have described. It would be desirable to extend and refine our measurements of golfer errors and characteristics of the grass. Variations of ball characteristics affect results somewhat and could be added to the model. In general, nearly all of the experimental results we describe could be repeated and extended for more accurate data. Numerical accuracy of our data is good in most essentials, but we accepted reasonable approximations, based on experiments where necessary, as being far better than no quantized information.

The USGA has issued limitations on flexibility of the head which have the effect of requiring head designs to be essentially rigid compared with the substantial deformation of the ball at impact. This is closely related to serious work of others with finite element analysis methods showing that most driver heads have almost negligible deformation relative to the ball and behave very nearly as a truly rigid body.

Thus we believe our treatment as a rigid body is a good approximation, and we expect that finite element analysis leads only to minor changes due to effects of deformation. Such analyses can help approximate optimum mass distribution in the head, but we think there is not much more to gain in that respect.

SOME EXAMPLES OF DRIVER SHOTS WITH OUR MODEL

WANT TO SOLVE MANY OF YOUR VEXING PROBLEMS? STUDY THESE EXAMPLES OF THE EFFECTS OF CHANGING LOFT ANGLE, FACE ANGLE, HEIGHT OF THE CENTER OF GRAVITY, HEAD SPEED, WIND, AND SOME OPTIMUM COMBINATIONS.

Our model, described in Chapter 2, allows us to change values for inputs, such as AA, cg, HS, HW, and LA which are defined below, and many more. We normally choose HS and other inputs to suit the golfer classes defined below. The model then gives CHD; LAE; initial and final flight conditions of the ball; details during the flight; bounce and roll after the flight; the point where the ball stops; and many more outputs. In this chapter, we will examine how some of the inputs, familiar to golfers, affect the outputs.

Table 3-1 shows the effects of changes in these inputs to our model on the shot and on the distance. Its caption gives more detail. The club used for these examples has a large, titanium head that we designed several years ago with a 46-inch graphite shaft. It is representative of modern drivers.

Notice that the numbers in bold print in the table identify the variables which were changed, in groups of 3 (or in one instance, 5) lines. You can compare corresponding effects caused by these input changes on the height, flight distance, and bounce and roll distance.

Lines 1-5 show that HS has a large effect on

CHD, as expected.

Remember that each case has LA which is optimized for that HS except for lines 12-20.

Lines 6-8 show the effect of lowering HW from 205 grams to 195 grams and lines 9-11 show the effect of increasing HW to 215 grams. HW has less effect on CHD than you might have expected. Lines 1-5 indicate that HS has a large effect, but of course, large HW reduces HS. The optimum combination will be discussed in later chapters.

Comparison of lines 12-14, 15-17, and 18-20 shows the effect of LA when it is not at its optimum value.

Comparison of lines 21-23 with lines 1, 3, and 5 shows the effect of lowering the location of a hit by .20 inch. This is governed by the relation between LA and cg location. Again there is an optimum combination for maximum distance and various other optimum combinations of design variables.

Other drivers will behave similarly but with somewhat different numbers because of differences of their design variables.

It is interesting, but perhaps not very useful, that the launch angle of the ball is always less than LA for all practical club designs.

Table 3-2 shows effects of weather conditions on flight of the ball. The bold numbers show the changes made from the first line, in groups of 2 lines. Many golfers know that balls go farther at high altitudes, as confirmed in the table. High air temperature increases distance and low temperature decreases it more than most golfers realize.

Most believe that high humidity reduces distance, but it has the opposite effect and the effect is very small. This is because humidity reduces air density. Contrary to popular opinion, humid air is slightly less dense than dry air.

Figure 3-1 depicts graphically some of the results of Table 3-1. It illustrates 3 different head designs, used by golfers A, B, and C, (defined above) whereas Table 3-1 was only for golfer B.

Figure 3-2 shows the effects of off-center hits for 3 bulge radii and for 3 roll radii. Notice that the optimized bulge radius (the 2 central views) greatly reduces the spread of stop points, but optimum roll radius mainly affects only distance. Both act together to some extent, so when combined, these are the best choices for this case. Chapter 18 explains our new and better way to determine the shape of the face surface.

Figure 3-3 shows behavior of hooks and slices. Unlike Figure 3-2, these are center hits for slice or hook swing types and AA was adjusted to bring the hooks and slices back to the target direction. Observation of such shots may give the impression that most of the lateral curvature is toward the end of the flight, but the curvature is actually reasonably constant throughout the flight.

It is conventional wisdom that a slight hook (a draw) with a driver will give a longer CHD than a slight slice (a fade), or even longer than a straight shot. Figure 3-3 illustrates that these ideas are not generally correct. It represents a driver designed with LA and cg location optimized for maximum CHD, which is our normal design goal.

It was usual for the cg of drivers to be much too high in driver heads designed 10 or 20 years ago; even now, the cg tends to be higher than optimum.

Even if the cg is properly located, a draw will give more distance than a fade if the golfer is using a driver with somewhat more than optimum LA, for the same reason. When (as is always preferable) the driver design has optimized LA and cg for the particular golfer class, straight shots give the longest CHD and essentially the same small loss of distance for either fades or draws.

This is not true for the fairway clubs which have LA much higher than for maximum CHD. For them, draws do give longer shots than straight shots. The reason is that LAE is lower when the golfer grips the club to cause a draw and the lower LAE adds distance, unlike the case of an optimized driver design.

Figure 3-4 is an example which represents a driver when the head wind is extreme, a condition which few golfers have tried. Behavior of the shot is generally very different from normal shots. The ball flies higher and actually flies back and bounces and rolls back toward the golfer at the end of the shot. At much lower HS, the great deviations from a normal shot are much reduced and at higher HS the deviations are greater. Use of a driver having exceptionally low LA reduces the loss of CHD.

Chapter 14 provides similar information for other clubs.

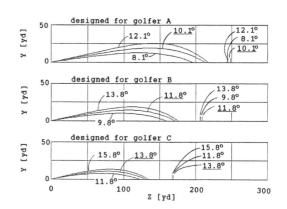

Fig. 3-1 *The relation among HS, LA, and CHD. LA is indicated on each trajectory. The "flagstick" at the right end of each trajectory is where the ball stops. The underlined numbers are for the design case and give best performance.*

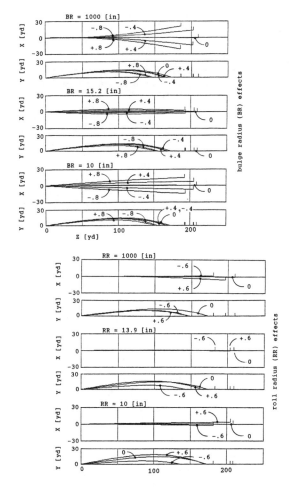

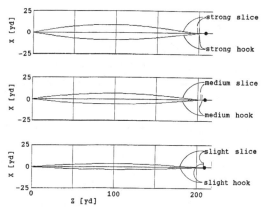

Fig. 3-3 *The effect of slices and hooks (or fades and draws) on CHD. For the curved shots, AA was adjusted so that they stopped in the target direction. Only strong hooks and slices have much effect on distance, slices being slightly worse than hooks for this particular club.*

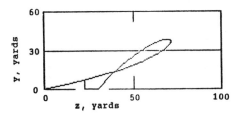

Fig. 3-4 *An example of extreme head wind. Here, a modern 46 inch driver was used with HS = 84.6 mph with a center hit directly into a 50 mph head wind. With 60 mph head wind, the ball lands 23 yards behind the golfer and rolls 27 more yards to the rear.*

Fig. 3-2 *The effect of bulge and roll. These are graphs of the plan and elevation views (top and side views) of the trajectory. Hit locations are shown in inches: at center of face (0), at the toe (–), at the heel (+), top (+), and bottom (–). In the 3 upper pairs of trajectories, bulge radius varies and hits vary in the toe-heel direction. In the 3 lower trajectories, roll varies and hits vary in the top-bottom direction. The model BWJ is shown as the 2 central views for which it is optimized, showing the degree of improvement which is practical.*

Table 3-1 *Effects of HW, HS, LA, and hit location above the cg on flight of the ball. The club is model BWJ designed for golfer B, but in each case, LA was adjusted to the optimum value for maximum CHD except for LA 16, 12, and 10 degrees. Bold numbers highlight the variables which change, usually in groups of 3 lines.*

club head variables					leaving the driver head				hitting the fairway				trajectory			stop point	
head weight gm	head speed mph	loft angle deg	face angle deg	distance above cg inches	velocity mph	spin rate rpm	azimuth deg	elevation deg	velocity mph	spin rate rpm	azimuth deg	elevation deg	maximum height yds	flight distance yds	B&R distance yds	CHD yds	line number
205	**50**	17.8	−1.4	0.04	68.6	2338	.5	15.0	49	2086	.3	−20.4	5.1	63.0	34.5	97.5	1
205	**70**	14.7	−1.1	0.04	97.5	2755	.5	12.6	54.5	2302	−.2	−24.1	10.0	120.4	36.5	156.9	2
205	**90**	12.0	−.9	0.04	126.7	2936	.5	10.6	56.4	2292	−.5	−29.5	16.8	183.1	34.0	217.2	3
205	**110**	10.4	−.8	0.04	155.6	3181	.6	9.5	57.3	2308	−.5	−38.0	27.7	242.6	27.9	270.4	4
205	**130**	9.0	−.7	0.04	184.6	3291	.7	8.5	59.8	2250	−.1	−44.4	39.7	292.0	23.4	315.4	5
195	50	17.6	−1.4	0.04	68.1	2302	.5	14.8	49.1	2060	.3	−20.0	4.9	61.5	34.8	96.2	6
195	90	12.1	−.9	0.04	125.5	2950	.5	10.7	56.3	2308	−.5	−29.4	16.6	180.8	34.0	214.8	7
195	130	9.0	−.7	0.04	183.0	3270	.7	8.5	59.6	2246	.3	−43.8	38.8	289.4	23.9	313.3	8
215	50	17.8	−1.4	0.04	69.1	2347	.5	15.0	49.1	2091	−.5	−20.6	5.2	64.2	34.5	98.6	9
215	90	11.9	−.9	0.04	127.7	2940	.5	10.6	56.5	2289	−.4	−29.9	17.2	185.5	33.8	219.3	10
215	130	8.3	−.6	0.04	186.5	3066	.7	8.0	60.3	2118	.3	−42.1	36.8	294.8	25.6	320.5	11
205	50	**16.0**	−1.3	0.04	69.2	2106	.6	13.5	51.1	1899	.3	−17.9	4.2	59.8	37.4	97.2	12
205	90	**16.0**	−1.3	0.04	124.4	3909	.5	13.8	51.9	2921	−.9	−41.6	25.5	181.8	22.9	204.7	13
205	130	**16.0**	−1.3	0.04	179.5	5773	.4	14.1	59.4	3757	−1.3	−59.6	65.9	241.0	10.3	251.3	14
205	50	**12.0**	−.9	0.04	70.4	1563	.5	10.3	56.5	1448	.3	−12.5	2.5	49.0	44.6	93.6	15
205	90	**12.0**	−.9	0.04	126.7	2936	.5	10.6	56.4	2292	−.5	−29.6	16.8	183.2	34.0	217.2	16
205	130	**12.0**	−.9	0.04	182.7	4389	.6	10.9	59.7	2880	−.9	−53.4	54.6	275.3	15.4	290.7	17
205	50	**10.0**	−.8	0.04	70.9	1280	.4	8.7	59.4	1203	.3	−10.1	1.7	41.9	48.3	90.2	18
205	90	**10.0**	−.8	0.04	127.5	2437	.6	9.0	61.4	1970	−.2	−22.6	12.2	173.2	42.5	215.6	19
205	130	**10.0**	−.8	0.04	184.1	3668	.7	9.3	59.6	2161	−.5	−48.2	45.3	288.4	20.0	308.4	20
205	50	15.8	−1.2	**−0.16**	69.3	2080	.5	13.4	51.3	1878	.3	−17.6	4.1	59.4	37.7	97.2	21
205	90	11.9	−.9	**−0.16**	126.7	2925	.5	10.6	56.5	2286	−.5	−29.4	16.7	183.0	34.2	217.2	22
205	130	9.3	−.7	**−0.16**	184.5	3394	.7	8.7	59.7	2307	−.2	−45.5	41.3	291.3	22.4	313.7	23
1 column number	**2**	**3**	**4**	**5**	**6**	**7**	**8**	**9**	**10**	**11**	**12**	**13**	**14**	**15**	**16**	**17**	

Table 3-2 *Effects of wind, weather, and altitude on flight of the ball. This is model BWJ as designed for golfer B. In all cases, the ball launch speed is 122.8 mph, 10.4 degrees upward and .5 degrees to the right, with backspin of 2788 rpm. The first line is the reference for all the others.*

environmental conditions					hitting the fairway				trajectory			stop point		
wind speed mph	wind direction	altitude feel	temperature deg F	% relative humidity	velocity mph	spin rate rpm	azimuth deg	elevation deg	maximum height yds	flight distance yds	B&R distance yds	distance to left yds	forward distance yds	radial distance yds
0	**-**	**0**	**70**	**20**	**57.3**	**2215**	**−.4**	**−26.9**	**14.6**	**172.6**	**36.5**	**0**	**209.2**	**209.2**
0	-	**2000**	70	20	59.9	2230	−.3	−25.1	13.9	173.5	39.8	1	213.2	213.2
0	-	**6000**	70	20	65.4	2262	−.2	−21.9	12.6	173.8	46.4	−.4	220.2	220.2
0	-	0	**50**	20	56.2	2209	−.4	−27.8	14.9	172.0	35.2	−.1	207.2	207.2
0	-	0	**100**	20	59.1	2225	−.3	−25.7	14.1	173.3	38.7	.1	212.0	212.0
0	-	0	70	**10**	57.3	2215	−.4	−26.9	14.6	172.5	36.5	0	209.1	209.1
0	-	0	70	**90**	57.6	2217	−.4	−26.7	14.5	172.7	36.9	0	209.6	209.6
10	**Head**	0	70	20	47.3	2163	−.7	−36.3	16.9	166.0	23.7	−.3	189.7	189.7
30	**Head**	0	70	20	34.2	2053	−4.5	−75.3	22.9	129.8	−4.1	−.5	125.7	125.7
10	**Tail**	0	70	20	62.4	2265	−.2	−21.1	27.7	173.5	48.6	.3	222.1	222.1
30	**Tail**	0	70	20	85.4	2355	0	−15.0`	9.9	164.3	69.5	.8	233.9	233.9
10	**From left**	0	70	20	58.0	2216	−8.6	−26.5	14.5	172.8	37.3	−15.6	209.4	210.0
30	**From left**	0	70	20	62.4	2234	−22.5	−23.8	13.8	171.6	42.6	−44.8	208.6	213.4

GOLFER ERRORS

THOSE OF YOU WHO ARE INCLINED TO ACCEPT YOUR "ALMOST GREAT SHOTS", HERE'S WHAT YOU'RE MISSING. READ ABOUT ACTUAL MEASUREMENTS OF HOW YOUR HITS SCATTER OVER A CLUB FACE, HOW MANY HITS YOU MAKE WHICH ARE PARTLY OFF THE FACE, GOLFER VARIATIONS IN HEAD SPEED, AIMING ERRORS, AND OTHERS.

INTRODUCTION

Determining the most important errors and working with them is, in some respects, the most important feature of our work. We classify errors into 2 types, input errors and output errors. Input errors cause output errors.

We measure output errors by how much the stop points of typical hits vary from perfect, error-free hits for the average head speed of the golfer being considered. This process allows us to evaluate the importance of various input errors. For example, stop point errors caused by a golfer's off-center hit can be compared with the stop point errors using a driver having loft angle different from what's best suited for that particular golfer.

There is no logic for directly comparing one error such as an off-center hit with another error such as a wrong loft angle other than to compare how

each input affects the output (the stop point of the shot). Use of a model such as ours allows many such comparisons. In many respects, this is the real need for a good model.

We classify golfer errors as input errors. Other input errors include such things as deviation of club design from optimum and environmental effects such as condition of the turf and effects of wind.

Errors and their importance to golfers are more fully covered in Chapters 6, 21, and 36.

To use the model for optimizing designs, we needed to evaluate golfer errors and to find which are the most important. It is the nature of the combination of errors that the most important few sources of input error combine to establish the resulting output errors (errors of stop points), with the numerous smaller errors contributing so little to the result that for most purposes they can be safely ignored.

We found nothing published on these golfer errors, so we measured them on actual golfers and determined which are worthy of including in the model. We are grateful to the numerous golfers who participated in these tests.

Throughout this book, you will find the theme and message that input errors causing small errors in the output usually should be ignored when there are other input errors causing much larger output errors. The first priority is to reduce effects of the most important input errors wherever that is possible. We didn't discover this, of course. It applies widely to all kinds of devices and systems, including design of balls and golf clubs, (and even social, economic and political systems, though often very difficult to apply.)

For example, if we assume you have a driver design well suited for your game, your own errors (golfer errors) are most important. The case where your driver design is poor and may cause larger errors

	SYMBOLS AND DEFINITIONS	
AA	[deg] the angle between the path of the clubhead at impact and the target direction, positive toward the left.*	
AHP	[deg] upward tilt of the long axis of the hit pattern.*	
CA	[deg] contact angle which is the acute angle between the direction of travel of the clubhead cg and a level plane at the time of impact.*	
CBS	[in] for putters, the vertical separation from sole line to bottom of ball, positive when the sole is above the bottom of the ball.	
dAA	[deg] standard deviation of AA.	
dHS	[%] standard deviation of HS just before impact as a percent of HS.	
dLA	[in] standard deviation of the center of impact locations (hit patterns) on the club face, measured in the direction of the long axis of the impact pattern. dLA is approximately in the toe-heel	

	direction.	
dSA	[in] the same as dLA but measured in the direction of the short axis of the hit pattern and is approximately in the up-down direction.	
dWA	[deg] for a golfer, the standard deviation of the rotation about the shaft axis from its mean value.	
HCP	handicap.	
HS	[mph] head speed, speed of the cg of the head at the time of impact.	
LA	[deg] loft angle.*	
LIA	[deg] lie angle.*	
SPA	[deg] swing plane angle between the normal to the swing plane and the Y axis.*	
POF hits	partly off the face hits for those hits near the edge of the face for which there is not a full circular imprint.	
*	*More detail will be found for these items in the Appendix.*	

than golfer errors is discussed in Chapter 21.

In approximate order of decreasing effects, the principal golfer errors are variations expressed as standard deviations: dAA, dHS, hit patterns on the long axis of the hit pattern (dLA), dWA, and hit patterns on the short axis of the hit pattern (dSA). The order of importance changes somewhat, principally with club selection. For design, dLA and dSA are very important, even though they usually cause smaller errors than the others. The reason is that their effects can be reduced by proper design, whereas little or nothing can be done about dWA, dHS, and dAA.

There is an additional penalty which is important for the medium and higher handicappers. That is POF hits which appear when dLA and dSA are large. The frequency of POF hits (partly off the face hits) can be greatly reduced by good design.

POF hits are very detrimental and are discussed below and in Chapter 17.

We were able to express these golfer errors in equations for use in our model, showing how they depend on HCP and LA as described in the Technical Notes.

Hit Pattern Errors

To measure the scatter of hits on the face, dLA and dSA, we applied hit tape which leaves an imprint of the impact after each hit. For these tests, 19 golfers made 50 hits each with a driver, 5-iron, and 9-iron. We measured the location of the center of each impact and studied the results statistically. Figure 4-1 shows a typical hit tape mark.

Figures 4-2, 4-3, and 4-4 show the general characteristics of the hit pattern as affected by HCP and club choice. In general the hit patterns are elliptical in shape with the long axis of the ellipses approximately perpendicular to the shaft axis. Thus, the patterns are tilted upward at the toe end, more for long clubs and less for the short irons.

dAA, dHS, and dWA Errors

We made many stroboscopic photos in dim light of the swings of numerous golfers hitting balls. The clubs and golfers had reflecting tape so we could make accurate measurements of their positions just prior to impact. This allowed us to measure the other 3 principal golfer errors, dAA, dHS, and dWA.

We studied them statistically and developed equations to show how they relate to golfer HCP.

POF Hits

Figure 4-2 shows that some hits are centered near the edge or off the face of a driver. We call them POF hits and figure 4-3 shows that they are common for golfers with a high HCP and much less so for those with a low HCP. These are among the worst hits which golfers can make. For drivers, POF hits are much reduced when the face is large, and when the face outline is oriented to conform approximately to the hit pattern distribution. POF hits, discussed in greater depth in Chapter 17, can be as important as the other golfer errors discussed here.

When the club design reduces POF hits substantially, it is a significant factor in improving confidence of the golfer with a higher HCP using the driver. This is an important, or perhaps the most important, reason that large driver heads have become popular in recent years, even though the importance of their large faces often is not recognized specifically.

Large heads also have large moment of inertia terms which enlarges the sweet spot and this is their other important advantage.

Creating a club to minimize errors and assure good distance for drives (and thus help golfer confidence) has been the motive for many design improvements. For example, the ill effects due to lack of confidence can be reduced for drivers by use of a large face which is easier to hit and by club design which minimizes scatter of shots due to off-center hits.

We have often had reports of golfers using our improved new driver stating that it seemed to improve their performance for the whole game.

Other Golfer Errors

There are many other golfer errors, some of which we measured and found small enough to disregard in our model. Many are important but difficult to measure, such as a golfer's confidence, health, and psychological state. Errors due to such factors were implicitly included in our golfer tests, since such things varied in a normal way among golfers tested.

We measured numerous additional golfer errors and believe they contribute so little to scatter of stop points of shots that they could reasonably be neglected. Furthermore, club design can do nothing to minimize their consequences.

By use of photographs, we measured the position of the eyes of a few golfers and found variations as they aimed their club time after time. There was no obvious way to reduce any errors this may cause in aiming.

We studied foot position. It is a part of AA which we did measure, but has no apparent other large effects and dAA accounts for its error contribution.

We studied factors which most golfers use when taking aim, including:

- *Perception of the orientation of the clubhead*
- *Appearance of the hands on the grip*
- *Exactly how the orientation of the grip and clubhead is chosen*
- *What factors they study in choosing their aiming direction*
- *Whether they swing outside-in or inside-out*
- *Whether they sole the driver on the turf at address or hover it behind the ball*
- *Where they tee up the ball relative to their feet and body and variations in this position*

We couldn't conceive design improvements which would significantly reduce the scatter of stop points of hits due to changes in such variables.

We believe a large clubhead can be oriented as desired more accurately than a small one, but we did not find that aim lines or other aiming or aligning features on the clubhead made a significant difference. *It seems likely that some aiming features may be beneficial, but only after the golfer has had much practice in their use, and time of practice is another factor we did not evaluate.*

FEEL, SOUND, AND APPEARANCE

We believe that things such as feel, sound of impact, and appearance are only important on a transient basis and are not particularly important design factors. We believe that when a golfer becomes familiar with the use of a club and believes that it performs well, the golfer will usually become accustomed to its feel, sound, and appearance and will come to consider these characteristics to be quite acceptable, even desirable. Accordingly, we consider them to have little long-term importance to club design, even though such attributes may have

promotional value for a manufacturer for a few years.

We distinguish between "swing feel" and "impact feel." Swing feel seems to be very dependent on shaft flexibility and seems to be basically a golfer's preference. Remember that some golfers have learned to make good shots with trick or practice demonstration shafts which have a hinge part way down the shaft. Chapters 19 and 20 discuss shaft characteristics and feel in more detail.

Impact feel has been discussed in terms such as "the best feel is no feel." However, some seem to believe that a prominent impact feel is helpful for golfers to detect whether or not they are hitting the sweet spot as desired. We suspect "no feel" is best or that a favorable feel is simply the feel most familiar to the golfer.

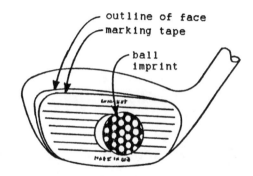

Fig. 4-1 *A typical hit tape imprint mark on a driver. We studied the diameters and locations of the centers of such imprints.*

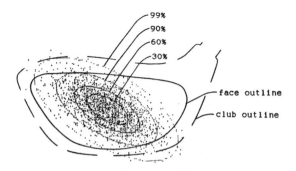

Fig. 4-2 *Typical distribution of hits on the face of a driver for a golfer of HCP=20, showing the elliptical distribution. Numbers on the ellipses indicate the percent of hits which will be inside of each ellipse. POF hits are indicated by the many dots near the edge or outside of the face for this HCP.*

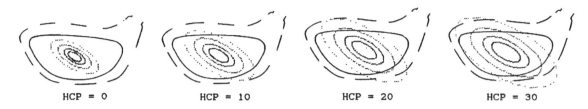

Fig. 4-3 *These ellipses show the same percentage distribution of hits on a driver as in Figure 4-2, and illustrate how they increase in size as HCP increases.*

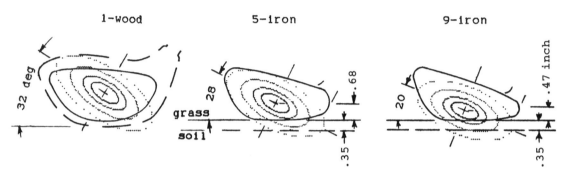

Fig. 4-4 *Hit patterns for various clubs. CLG affects the tilt angle of the ellipses and has only a small effect on the size and proportions of the ellipses. All are for HCP 20 and the ellipses are as in Figure 4-2. The long axis of the ellipse tends to be perpendicular to the shaft axis. LA is also related to the length and thus to the orientation of the shaft axis, and we happened to choose to define the tilt as a function of LA rather than CLG.*

TECHNICAL NOTES

For measurements in any field of endeavor, there is probably an infinite series of error sources. When input errors are independent of each other and are considered in order of decreasing effect on the output, a rapidly converging series results.

In the cases of variables related to one another (as is true of most variables), our model treats them appropriately. For example when 2 inputs do nearly the same thing, the first one considered generally predominates if nearly equal in size. Otherwise, both make appropriate contributions with the result that the model has no concern for interrelation of errors.

Other variables must be considered independently. For example, consider lack of confidence. The reasons why a golfer is less confident than normal could depend on many things, such as who are the competitors, how serious are the consequences of the game, how tired the golfer is, the golfer's current mental state, etc.

Each of these in turn may depend on other items on the list and on many additional factors. While confidence (unmeasurable as it may be) depends on various other factors, it is probably an important factor in causing variations in such variables as deviations of dHS, dAA, and dWA.

Fortunately, only the few most important errors are needed for most work with error analysis because they mask the smaller ones.

This reasoning, supported by tests with our computer model, helped us choose the 5 principal errors (dLA, dSA, dAA, dWA, and dHS) and to disregard other golfer errors.

Beyond this, we know of no way that club design can suppress effects of many very important error sources such as golfer health and psychology. An exception is golfer confidence which is improved by good design to minimize scatter of stop points and by reducing POF hits for drivers.

Almost no quantitative information has been published on the nature of golfer errors and how they combine. In most of our tests with golfers, only about 20 golfers were involved, each usually making numerous hits.

Figures 4-2, 4-3, and 4-4 show conventional clubs at their normal lie angles as measured in the head frame.

We believe use of dim light for strobe photos made our measurements of dWA less accurate than we would like. The golfer must be able to clearly perceive the orientation of the clubhead relative to his hands as essential parts of his control over dWA, and this is more difficult in dim light. This is a relatively minor problem with dAA and dHS.

More tests would be highly desirable to refine the expressions below, but reasonably accurate expressions soundly based are adequate for our purposes. They are far better than good experience and good estimates. Good estimates are impossible in many cases because of testing difficulties and the great complexity of most of the interactions of variables.

In summary of our tests, the following equations were incorporated into our model for drivers and irons. Included are golfer errors which are essential inputs for our model.

Putter errors are discussed in Chapters 28, 29, 34, and 35.

(1) $dLA = SQR(rn * area/\pi)$ [in].

(2) $dSA = SQR(area/(rn * \pi))$ [in]; where both dLA and dSA include small effects of dWA on hit pattern size;
     $area = .1094 - .00218 * HCP * (.028 * LA - 6.1)$ [sq in]; and $rn = 2.37 - .00538 * LA$ [].

(3) Ych is height of the center of the hit pattern ellipse above the sole line of the clubhead. It is half of the face height for drivers. Note: for irons, refer to Chapter 24.

(4) $AHP = -35.4 + .306 * LA$ [deg], angle of the hit pattern (see Appendix 1).

(5) $CBS = .84 * (1 - sinLA) - Ych$ [in] for non-drivers and 0 for drivers, where CBS is vertical separation from sole line to bottom of ball.

(6) $WA = 0$ [deg].

(7) $WAR = .122 * HS - .957$ [deg/sec].

(8) $dWA = 1.42 + .0412 * HCP$ [deg/sec].

(9) $dHS = 2.984 + .0868 * HCP$ [%].

(10) $dAA = 2.314 + .0673 * HCP$ [deg].

(11) $AA = 0$ [deg].

(12) $CA = 1.7$ for a driver [yd].

(13) $SPA = arccos(BAS/HYP)$ [deg], the swing plane angle, where
     GH is golfer height [in],
     ATH is additional tee height above
       2-1/8 inch tee [in],
     $HYP = 16.1 * GH/72 + CLG$ [in],
     $AAD = D(173) * D(172) - ATH$ [in], and
     $BAS = sqr(HYP^2 - AAD^2)$ [in].

SCATTER OF STOP POINTS

SHOTS WIND UP IN VARIOUS PLACES, OF COURSE. HERE ARE EXAMPLES OF WHICH GOLFER ERRORS CAUSE WHAT SCATTER OF STOP POINTS AND HOW SUCH ERRORS COMBINE TO CONFOUND YOUR BEST PLANS FOR A SHOT.

Our model is useful for graphic displays such as stop points of hits. In one program option an input can be changed and the model shows the effect on the scatter of stop points. For this chapter we used this option to plot the stop points when some or all of the 5 golfer errors defined in Chapter 4 were present. The result is interesting pictures of the kinds of disturbance to the stop point caused by these 5 errors.

Figure 5-1 provides such pictures for 2 different driver designs and for a 5-iron and a 9-iron. All were for golfer B. The captions define the 2 drivers.

The top set of graphs are for only the standard deviation dAA acting. It causes mainly lateral errors as expected.

The 2nd set of graphs are for dHS and it shows that dHS causes primarily only distance variations.

The graphs for standard deviation of hit patterns on dLA show much distance variation and little lateral variation except for the poor design of driver B (a laminated wood head from around 1985).

The graphs for dWA and dSA show effects which are less obvious. The scatter is smaller for the irons mainly because they have smaller CHD. The dWA error scatter for the 5 iron and particularly the 9 iron in Figure 5-1 is strongly tilted compared with the other clubs.

Figure 5-2 shows how these errors combine as variables are removed from the test. Going down from the top graph (which contains all 5 principal errors), the 2nd graph shows somewhat less scatter as dSA is removed, then progressively less scatter until the lowest graph, with the least scatter, due only to dAA.

Face surface shape mainly reduces only the effects of dLA and dSA as discussed in more detail in Chapter 18. This is clearly shown in Figure 5-3 which compares the modern design driver A with the 1985-vintage driver B which has a poorer face surface shape. Moment of inertia also accounts for some of the differences.

Figure 5-4 shows the effect with all 5 errors, for 4 golfer classes, A, B, and C (as used in Figure 3-1 in Chapter 3) and P (a professional golfer) and for the same 4 clubs, drivers A and B, a 5-iron and a 9-iron. Figure 5-4 is a useful general summary of the scatter patterns in real golf.

The Technical Notes give more detail about the scatter of stop points for shots to a green.

SYMBOLS AND DEFINITIONS

CHD [yd] the distance of a hit at the face center with no golfer errors.*

dAA [deg] standard deviation of AA.

dHS [%] standard deviation of HS just before impact as a percent of HS.

dLA [in] standard deviation of the center of impact locations (hit patterns) on the club face, measured in the direction of the long axis of the impact pattern. dLA is approximately in the toe-heel direction.

dSA [in] the same as dLA but measured in the direction of the short axis of the hit pattern and is approximately in the up-down direction.

dWA [deg] for a golfer, the standard deviation of the rotation about the shaft axis from its mean value.

golfer P a representative golfer with CHD=281 yards and HS=114.1 mph on our Reference T driver and with HCP=0.

golfer A a representative golfer with CHD=251 yards and H=100.7 mph on our Reference T driver and with HCP=10.

golfer B a representative golfer with CHD=217 yards and HS=87.2 mph on our Reference T driver and with HCP=20.

golfer C a representative golfer with CHD=179 yards and HS=73.8 mph on our Reference T driver and with HCP=27.5.

HCP handicap.

LA [deg] loft angle.*

* More detail will be found for these items in the Appendix.

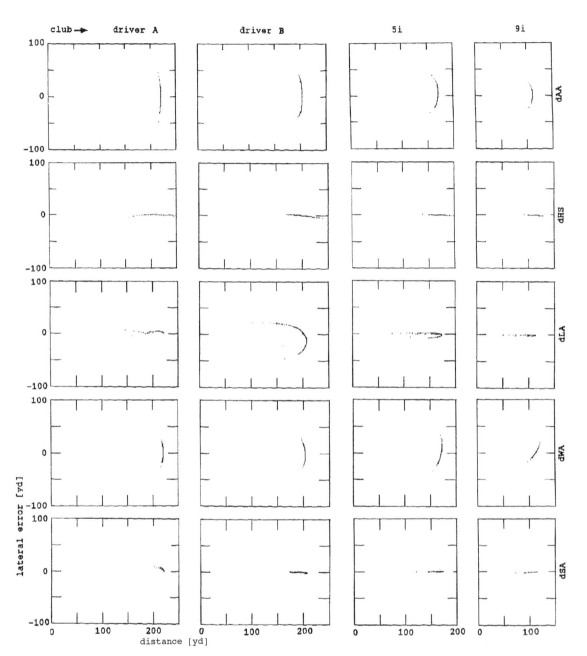

Fig. 5-1 *250 stop points for each error when all other errors are zero for golfer B with various clubs. Driver A is our optimized large head driver design. Driver B is a laminated wood head from around 1985.*

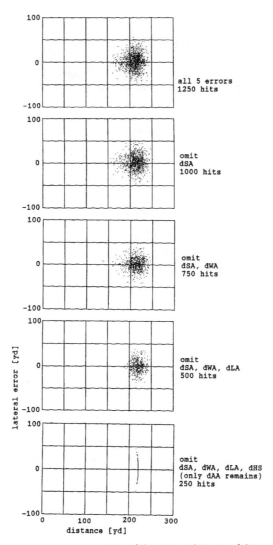

Fig. 5-2 *How individual errors combine to cause scatter of the stop points on a fairway for golfer B with driver A.*

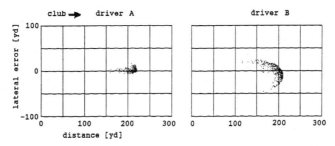

Fig. 5-3 *The effect of improved club design on scatter due to only dLA and dSA (hit pattern) for golfer B with improved driver A and driver B, an obsolete laminated wood design.*

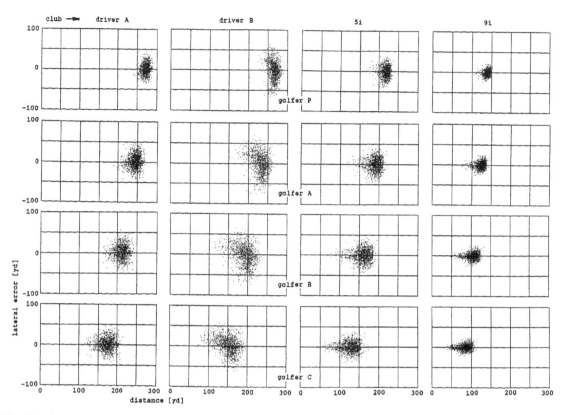

Fig. 5-4 *A general comparison of the scatter of stop points for 4 levels of golfer skill. Each pattern represents 1250 hits.*

TECHNICAL NOTES

Reference 9 in pages 24 and 25 indicated groupings of stop points for iron shots to the green. Scatter was in 2 lobes, one well to the right and one to the left of the flag with prominent differences as compared to the sparse groupings in the vicinity of the flag.

The results combined averages of tour players on many holes, were for full shots relatively far from the green, and were based on thousands of observations. It is significant that they were deviations from the flag, and the intended aim points for each shot evidently were not known and thus not considered.

However, the flag is often not the golfers' aim point. The main reason for this is that flag placements are often near one side or the other in tournaments. For this reason, this kind of scatter of stop points might reasonably be expected. It does not represent scatter from a golfer's intended aim point.

In order to be comparable to the scatter of individual shots such as we show in Figure 5-4, the aim point must be identified and all shots must be compared for one golfer or very similar golfers on one hole.

Our modeling represents the problem a golfer faces and describes the scatter the golfer must expect. There is no physical reason to expect the 2-lobed distribution in such cases and therefore, it is not at odds with our calculations of scatter.

In regard to partial swings, it is interesting that Reference 9 shows that the dense groupings are short and long rather than side to side. This is probably explained by flag placements near the back or front edge of the green.

We ran cases for full shots with HCP of −3 and found average distance scatter of 2% and lateral scatter of 3.5% of shot distance. These numbers compare with respective stated values of 1 to 2% and 7 to 9% given in Reference 9. There was fair agreement in distance and disagreement for lateral scatter as discussed here.

Part Two

Drivers, Fairway Woods, and Irons

THE NEED FOR A PERFORMANCE RATING

WE'LL SHOW YOU HOW BETTER GOLF CLUB DESIGN CAN IMPROVE YOUR ACCURACY AND DISTANCE. TO MEASURE THE IMPROVEMENT, WE'VE COME UP WITH A WAY TO DEFINE A SINGLE RATING NUMBER WHICH MEASURES PERFORMANCE OF ANY CLUB DESIGN.

A performance rating is essential for optimizing designs and is interesting in its own right. Although most useful when choosing a new driver or other club, you may also want to know how your driver compares with others and whether or not a driver with a better rating might be a factor in helping you improve your drives.

For our research, a rating serves an essential purpose, since it is impossible to use computer models to find optimum values of design variables

SYMBOLS AND DEFINITIONS

AR [yd] accuracy rating for drivers.*

ARP [yd] same as accuracy rating but includes POF effects.

cg [ ] center of gravity (more accurately, center of mass); its location is usually given in inches.

CHD [yd] center hit distance.*

CLG [in] club length.*

DE [yd] distance error, the distance by which a given driver's CHD stops short of CHD for a Reference D drive.*

golfer P a representative golfer with CHD=281 yards and HS=114.1 mph on our Reference T driver and with HCP=0.

golfer A a representative golfer with CHD=251 yards and H=100.7 mph on our Reference T driver and with HCP=10.

golfer B a representative golfer with CHD=217 yards and HS=87.2 mph on our Reference T driver and with HCP=20.

golfer C a representative golfer with CHD=179 yards and HS=73.8 mph on our Reference T driver and with HCP=27.5.

FA [deg] face angle.*

HCP [ ] handicap.

HS [mph] head speed, speed of the cg of the head just prior to impact.

HW [gm] head weight (mass), weight of the head without shaft.

LA [deg] loft angle.*

ME [yd] most probable error of stop points, taken to be the average error, measured from the stop point of an error-free center hit.*

MEP [yd] same as ME but effects of POF hits are included.

POF hits partly off the face hits for those hits near the edge of the face for which there is not a full circular imprint.

reference D driver imaginary ultimate driver design having 40 gram shaft, CLG=48 inches, 180 gram head, and 20 gram grip, design optimized for each HS in question.

reference T driver a driver with 88 gram graphite shaft, CLG = 43 inches, HW=200 grams, and 43.5 gram grip which we used in golfer tests and for frequent reference. Notice that modern drivers usually give up to 5 yards greater CHD than this reference.

Xcg [in] X location of the cg in the head frame, see Fig 2-1.

Ycg [in] Y location of the cg in the head frame, see Fig 2-1.

Zcg [in] Z location of the cg in the head frame, normally negative, see Fig 2-1.

More detail will be found for these items in the Appendix.

until an optimum result has been defined (a "rating"). Once this is defined, the design variables can be adjusted until the rating is as close as possible to the desired value.

For a driver, the two main goals are maximum distance and minimum scatter of stop points. Thus, we believe that only these 2 factors are needed to define best performance. One factor considers the distance of a center hit for a given HS and a given set of club design variables when there are no golfer errors and how near it comes to the CHD of a perfectly optimized driver. The other factor is the amount of scatter of the stop points when the important golfer errors are present. The following comments and the Technical Notes give more detail about how these 2 factors are measured and how they are combined into a single performance rating.

We consider scatter of the stop points of shots in 2 different ways. One disregards effects of POF hits and the other includes them. We call these AR for accuracy rating, and ARP for accuracy rating when effects of POF hits are considered. Thus, AR is simpler to calculate and is always smaller than ARP, but ARP is more meaningful for golfers.

The discussion above applies to the maximum distance clubs, namely the driver and the first fairway wood. For all of the more lofted clubs, if more distance is needed, you need only choose a less lofted club. The result is that AR and ARP for the other clubs consider only the scatter and omit the consideration of achieving maximum distance. Chapter 21 considers AR and ARP in greater depth for drivers, and Chapter 36 explains a performance rating for putters.

With our definition of the rating, the ideal value for the performance rating is zero, but real designs and golfer errors preclude a value of zero. The design goal is to minimize the performance rating, be it AR or ARP.

Our performance rating depends on the golfer's handicap (HCP) and head speed (HS). Accordingly, we often calculate a different performance rating for each of the golfers: P, A, B, or C. We arbitrarily defined them as 4 idealized golfers representing a scale of ability ranging from a scratch golfer (with a 0 HCP and a high HS) to a high scoring golfer (with a 27.5 HCP and a low HS).

Thus, our AR is suitable for a given class of golfer but not for golfers of all HCP and HS. In other words, a driver should be designed for a particular HCP and HS.

However, such a design is also quite satisfactory for a wide range of HCP, and for a moderate range of HS which is near the design values. When the appropriate details are calculated or measured for a given driver design, our model allows us to calculate its AR and ARP for any HS, such as for golfers P, A, B, and C.

It is possible to find AR and ARP by experiments with an actual driver and many hits by many golfers, but this is prohibitively complicated and inaccurate because of the extensive experiments needed and the variations among golfers, atmospheric conditions, conditions of fairways, etc. It is important to realize that the model will also do the job in a strictly objective manner if the user is objective with inputs.

TECHNICAL NOTES

Above, we said that we considered 2 factors for defining the performance rating. One is distance error (DE). The other is scatter of stop points. We measure scatter by most probable error of stop points either without considering POF hits (ME) or with POF hits considered (MEP).

For all clubs other than maximum distance clubs (driver and 1st fairway wood), DE is not important and MEP or ME are suitable ratings. For these clubs, MEP treats hitting too low on the face and hitting too far into the turf as POF hits. DE doesn't matter because distance is easily controlled by using a longer or shorter club.

We considered the best way to combine both factors for drivers. It is a mistake to design only for maximum distance or only for minimum scatter of stop points. The best choice is a rating factor which gives a reasonable compromise between distance and accuracy.

After some study for drivers, we chose to define AR as the mean value of DE and ME and ARP as the mean value of DE and MEP. Thus, AR = (DE+ME)/2 and ARP = (DE+MEP)/2. DE is the same whether or not POF hits are considered.

Ratings for putters are different and are considered in Chapter 36.

With drivers, for the DE part of AR we usually use the maximum feasible distance for a center hit with that particular shaft, head weight (HW), and head speed (HS), as if it had optimum loft angle (LA), face angle (FA), and center of gravity (cg) location. We then define DE as the amount by which a center hit fails to reach this maximum feasible distance. Notice that this maximum distance depends on the HS for which the club is being designed; we respected this requirement with the result that driver designs are optimized for each of several ranges of HS.

For most cases of comparison among drivers, we altered this somewhat so that we compared all drivers with reference D driver or with a similar one having a Grafalloy Attack Lite shaft, CLG = 46 inches, and HW = 180 grams. Thus, DE values vary.

This represents a close approach to maximum achievable distance, but with somewhat shorter shaft and lower HW which are near or above the upper limit of practicality. As explained in Table 20-2 (rounded numbers), the maximum realizable distance happens with impractical values of CLG = 50.3 inches and HW = 192 grams. This means that all other combinations of values for CLG and HW will give less center hit distance (longer, shorter, heavier, or lighter).

Our computer program for the model is designed to efficiently calculate a large number of hits with the important golfer errors present having random values which conform to their statistical distribution. The program finds the mean value of the radial distance of these stop points from the center hit location and this is our ME. That is, ME is the average deviation of all individual hits from the center hit and we call it the "most probable error."

DE depends only on the behavior of center hits. ME depends on the golfer's 5 principal errors. Both depend on HS, and on the club design. ME depends on face surface shape, moments of inertia, LA, and cg location. MEP is the same except for additionally considering POF effects.

A designer knows he wants a driver design that has the best possible accuracy and distance. He may have other preferences which tend not to be logically based, such as not deviating too far from currently accepted appearance, HW, and CLG.

Often production costs or cosmetic considerations are important. The United States Golf Association (USGA) Rules of Golf must be respected. Even with such requirements, the design can do better by having a single rating so he can judge when he has optimized his design as measured by this rating, having separately adjusted for his preferences as desired.

AR or ARP described in this Chapter serves the purpose of defining optimal performance. The rating could be modified and adjusted somewhat so long as it appropriately considers distance and accuracy.

AR or ARP can be found for an existing club, using our model or some reasonable equivalent. Required data for the club design for use of the model are:

- Measurement of the 6 moment of inertia terms for the driver head, the mass and center of gravity (cg) location of the head, the face surface shape, and shaft mounting details;

- After cutting the shaft to length, measurements of mass and cg location and the moment of inertia about an axis perpendicular to its long axis, mass per unit length at the tip (additional mass distribution items are unimportant), and its bending stiffness near the tip (discussed in greater detail in Chapter 19);

- Specification of the mass of the grip only, since its contribution to the inertia of the system is very small;

- And a number of others.

A case could be made for using this rating or some variation of it as an industry standard, in the interests of uniform information for the golfer. To do so on an existing product requires perhaps 10 to 20 hours of work, since each design requires the numerous measurements described above.

AR or ARP serve well for optimizing our designs. As discussed above, we modified these performance ratings somewhat for irons, and used a rather different rating method for putters as described in Chapter 36.

In our design work, analysis of the physical design of a clubhead is done in a sub-model which finds the mass properties for a given physical form of the head, for use in the main model.

The main model provides guidance for the optimum mass properties, based on many initial explorations by the designer (manual iterations). Inputs to define the physical form for the mass properties sub-model are manually adjusted to approximate such guidance from the main model. These results are then used to find the rating.

In practice Xcg, face angle, club length, head weight, lie angle and most other variables are usually determined separately to approximately match optimum values.

The program then uses the Simplex method to automatically find the optimum values for loft angle (LA), Ycg, Zcg, and sometimes values of other variables for center hits only.

The entire process is repeated many times to adjust the mass properties to approximate the optimum values.

Finally, the face surface shape, requiring 4 to 8 more variables, is found by additional use of the Simplex method in several stages.

VARIABLES WHICH AFFECT SHOT DISTANCE

I T'S NOT WEIGHT OR AGE OR FITNESS OR SEX THAT HAS THE BIGGEST EFFECT ON DISTANCE OF DRIVES. HERE YOU FIND WHICH ITEMS ARE THE BIGGIES AND WHICH ARE UNIMPORTANT.

This chapter summarizes the effects of the most important variables which affect shot distance. Most of these effects are well known by experienced golfers.

This list shows the variables in approximate order of importance, and suggests some of the interdependence of the variables. Note that other variables, those which produce smaller, negligible, effects, are not listed.

1. *HS, which depends on other variables including golfer performance, CLG, HW, and shaft weight and its weight distribution.*

2. *LA, which depends on distance desired and other design variables.*

3. *HW, whose optimum value depends mainly on CLG.*

4. *Off-center hits, which depend on golfer performance.*

5. *Slope of the landing area, a subject not studied here.*

6. *Ball characteristics, which depend on coefficients of restitution, dimple pattern, radius of gyration and other details (these are discussed in Chapter 26).*

7. *Atmospheric conditions, including wind, altitude, temperature, and humidity.*

Thus, items 1, 2, and 3 are usually much more important than the others, and HS usually is the most important of these. When a driver is optimized for maximum distance, all 3 of these variables are strongly related to one another.

In our model, only a few groups of variables including those defining golfer class, ball characteristics, and atmospheric conditions, are independent of the other groups. Some of these variables depend on numerous additional variables not listed, such as material characteristics of the head and all of the dimensional data on the head.

Golfers know that off-center hits reduce distance. The reduction increases, not merely in proportion to the off-center distance, but progressively faster as distance from the center increases.

Off-center hits are usually a rather small problem for good golfers. For less skilled golfers and beginners, off-center hits are more important. For high HCP golfers with more POF hits, they can cause more scatter than any other errors.

We believe that partly off the face (POF) hits have not received adequate attention in driver head design. They are discussed in greater detail in Chapter 17.

The main consideration of shaft selection is that a light shaft allows the golfer to obtain higher HS than a heavy shaft. The shaft should be reasonably stiff, particularly for strong hitters. The optimum combination of shaft length and HW was discussed in Chapter 2.

As was shown in Table 3-2, wind is the most important atmospheric condition and altitude is moderately important. Air temperature and humidity are less important. Altitude becomes rather important above 2 or 3 thousand feet. When the altitude is high, such as 5,000 feet or greater, a strong golfer can

---

SYMBOLS AND DEFINITIONS

cg   [] center of gravity (more accurately, center of mass); its location is usually given in inches.

CHD   [yd] center hit distance.*

CLG   [in] club length.*

HS   [mph] head speed, speed of the cg of the head just prior to impact.

HW   [gm] head weight (mass), weight of the head without shaft.

LA   [deg] loft angle.*

LAE   [deg] effective LA, somewhat different from LA because centrifugal force bends the shaft and at impact, somewhat changes clubhead orientation and clubhead rotation also affects it.*

POF hits   partly off the face hits.*

* More detail will be found for these items in the Appendix.

gain 10 yards or more on his driving distance. The percentage gain is somewhat less for a weaker golfer. The cause of more distance is reduced air drag on the ball resulting from lower air density at high altitudes.

Air temperature has a modest effect if the ball temperature doesn't change. CHD is somewhat greater in hot air than in cold air. This is because air density is less in hot air than in cold air.

Temperature of the ball affects its coefficients of restitution, an effect we have not studied. What is published indicates that warm balls travel considerably farther than cold balls. Ball temperature may cause larger effects than air temperature.

It may be surprising that humidity has only a very small effect on distance. This is because it has little effect on both air density and viscosity. Although it is commonly believed that humid air is heavier than dry air, the opposite is true. An increase of humidity causes a small decrease in air density, counter to general opinion, and thus a slight increase in distance.

Spin is very important but we did not include it directly in the variables list because spin is entirely governed by other inputs and the model automatically determines its value.

LAE is the main item which causes spin. In this case, it is what is known as "backspin." HS is also important for spin, because for a given loft, more HS will also cause faster spin.

Whether the ball is hit high or low on the face also has a rather important effect on spin. No ordinary kind of hit can reverse backspin, i.e., produce "over spin." Over spin can only be produced when the ball is launched somewhat downward, such as with negative LA, or is topped so badly that the ball is hit above its center.

So, is there an optimum rate of spin for drives in order to achieve maximum distance? Yes. Spin adds drag, increases height, and reduces distance. Too little spin gives less drag but insufficient height for best distance. The optimum spin is closely related to other variables, so it cannot be optimized independently. The related variables must be included in optimizing spin.

The designer can mainly design for the optimum by adjustment of LA and cg location, depending on the golfer class for which he is designing.

Side spin for center hits is caused when the face is not perpendicular to the line of travel of the clubhead at impact. Otherwise, for center hits, there is little or no side spin.

Side spin is the result of a faulty clubhead orientation at address, causing the club face to be too far open or closed at impact. The swing and/or the clubhead orientation are deliberately changed by good golfers to alter side spin and thus to make a curved shot when desired, as further discussed in Chapter 25.

Chapter 9 discusses numerical results of various changes in ball speed, launch angle, and backspin.

This discussion of side spin is for center hits. Off-center hits toward the toe or heel also cause side spin as discussed in Chapter 18.

EFFECTS OF LOFT ANGLE AND CENTER OF GRAVITY ON DRIVES

THERE'S MUCH TALK ABOUT LOFT ANGLE, CENTER OF GRAVITY LOCATION, WIND, PLAYING THE BALL BACK OR MORE FORWARD. HERE YOU'LL FIND OUT ALL THESE FUNDAMENTALS FOR DRIVERS.

HS, HW, LA, and cg location are the principal variables affecting the distance of a golf shot. For a given golfer class, HS depends strongly on HW and shaft weight and length. Most of this chapter is widely known in general terms but little has been published in quantitative forms such as the graphs and tables given here. These results come directly from our computerized model and give good qualitative support for our modeling. It is impractical to observe many of these effects directly with golfers or golfing machines.

The LA for best CHD depends strongly on HS and on the location of the cg in the clubhead. The best LA for a given HS may vary by several degrees between 2 different brands of drivers, unless their designs are nearly identical. The latter is rarely the case.

Thus, LA alone is an inadequate basis for choosing a driver because the cg location and other design variables are generally never the same for different drivers.

There are unique values for LA and Ycg for maximum distance for each driver design when its other head and shaft details are given. Optimized designs for low HS are somewhat different from the designs for high HS.

RESULTS WITH VARYING LOFT ANGLES

Figure 8-1 shows the general relation among HS, LA, and CHD for a modern driver having high inertia values and a rather high cg location. Only center hits are considered. There is a curve for a very slow swing of 60 mph. The other 4 curves are for golfers P, A, B, and C. Other drivers have somewhat different curves.

From the graph, LA should be about 18 degrees for maximum CHD, for HS = 60 mph. LA should be about 10 degrees for the fast swing of golfer P and the line shows optimum LA for other HS for this particular driver. All drivers show similar behavior. The effects of changes in LA are much greater for compact heads having low moments of inertia. Thus, optimum LA was more critical with early, compact heads.

FLIGHT DISTANCE

Figure 8-2 shows the percentage of the total distance of center hits for drivers which is due to flight of the ball. The remainder is for the bounce and roll on the fairway (ZBR). The strong hitters as shown for golfer P always get most of their distance in the air, especially at higher LA. Their flight distances are usually about 90% of their total distance. A slow hitter has flight distance which is about 70% of total. Driver design has a small effect on these curves.

These ZBR values are based on our experimental

SYMBOLS AND DEFINITIONS	
cg [ ] center of gravity (more accurately, center of mass); its location is usually given in inches.	**golfer C** a representative golfer with CHD = 179 yards and HS = 73.8 mph on our Reference T driver and with HCP = 27.5.
CHD [yd] center hit distance.*	
CLG [in] club length.*	**reference T driver** a driver with 88 gram graphite shaft, CLG = 43 inches, HW = 200 grams, and 43.5 gram grip which we used in golfer tests and for frequent reference. Notice that modern drivers usually give up to 5 yards greater CHD than this reference.
HCP handicap.	
HS [mph] head speed, speed of the cg of the head just prior to impact.	
HW [gm] head weight (mass), weight of the head without shaft.	
LA [deg] loft angle.*	
golfer P a representative golfer with CHD = 281 yards and HS = 114.1 mph on our Reference T driver and with HCP = 0.	**Xcg** [in] X location of the cg in the head frame, see Fig 2-1.
	Ycg [in] Y location of the cg in the head frame, see Fig 2-1.
golfer A a representative golfer with CHD = 251 yards and HS = 100.7 mph on our Reference T driver and with HCP = 10.	**Zcg** [in] Z location of the cg in the head frame, normally negative, see Fig 2-1.
golfer B a representative golfer with CHD = 217 yards and HS = 87.2 mph on our Reference T driver and with HCP = 20.	**ZBR** [yd] bounce and roll distance for clubs other than putters, measured from where the ball hits down and the flight (carry) ends.*
	More detail will be found for these items in the Appendix.

measurements on a level fairway in good condition. Chapter 2 gives more detail about ZBR. Fairways in various conditions give considerable variation of ZBR. Iron shots that are intended to land on a green use a different form of ZBR, and putts, still another.

EFFECT OF WIND

Wind has a large effect on the optimum LA for a driver. Figure 8-3 shows this effect for golfers C and A, and demonstrates the importance of using low LA when hitting into a strong head wind and high LA for strong tail wind. These trends are as expected. For driver designs with different cg locations, the curves are shifted upward or downward a small amount, but the trends are the same.

For drivers, Figure 8-4 shows more about the effect of head wind and following wind. Notice that the solid curves are for the optimum LA of Figure 8-3 for each wind speed and the dotted curves are for using LA optimized only for zero wind speed.

For example, this shows that golfers might want to hit from the tee with a 3, 4, or 5 wood with a strong following wind. It will give less HS than a driver, but the shot is much higher and will gain distance, as most golfers know.

Aerodynamic effects are much greater for high ball speed than for low ball speed. Thus, short hits with low ball speed are much less affected by wind. Very strong hitters need to be much more concerned with wind. Chapter 15 gives more detail about wind effects.

DETAIL ABOUT LA AND CG

LA and cg are so important that more detail is worthwhile. Figure 8-5 has graphs for each of the 3 HS values of golfers C, B, and A.

In all cases, the center of gravity is 1.02 inch rearward from the bottom of the club face. That is, $Zcg = -1.02$ inch. For each speed, there is a curve for each of 3 different values of Ycg at .47, .79 and 1.10.

The 3 graphs in Figure 8-5 have a definite trend from 73.8 to 100.7 mph. You can see the value of LA for each curve which gives maximum distance. This value of LA changes with HS and with Ycg.

We calculated the optimum combination of LA and Ycg values for this specific club for each of the 3 HS values. We found that the optimum LA decreases as HS increases (as is known) and also the

optimum location of Ycg is near .5 inch for this example and depends little on HS.

The value of Zcg for Figure 8-5 is typical of driver heads.

In order to show how Zcg affects the optimum (using golfer P), we calculated the curves shown in Figures 8-6 and 8-7. They are to be compared to the 100.7 mph curves in Figure 8-5.

Zcg of zero is similar to a 1-iron. Its center of gravity is typically in or near the face. Figure 8-6 shows that this causes both the optimum Ycg and the optimum LA (for maximum distance) to be much higher than when Zcg is farther back such as for a driver as shown in the right graph in Figure 8-5. This correctly suggests that center hits with a 1-iron can give about as much distance as a driver when each has its optimum LA and Ycg, and the same shaft length and head weight (which is not usual with conventional designs). In summary, maximum CHD depends little on Zcg, provided the best values for Ycg and LA are chosen to suit the value for Zcg; maximum CHD is much reduced with poor values of Ycg and LA.

As discussed later, a well-designed driver gives less scatter for off-center hits as compared with a long iron.

For Figure 8-7, we moved the cg unusually far toward the rear, to have $Zcg = -1.34$ inch. This caused both the optimum Ycg and the optimum LA to be much lower.

Table 8-1 shows optimum designs for maximum distance in Figures 8-5, 8-6, and 8-7.

These cases show an important fact: LA alone is a poor basis for choosing a driver for a given golfer, contrary to the judgment of most golfers. This is because Ycg and Xcg affect optimum LA rather strongly. When Zcg is rather far back, optimum LA is much decreased and optimum Ycg is lower.

Drivers usually have a marking which gives the LA. CLG (club length) is easy to measure. However, on most clubs, specific information about the location of the cg, the moment of inertia variables, shaft stiffness, and even the head weight is usually omitted. LA alone doesn't provide accurate information to help select a driver, so we developed a better guide than LA which we call the CHD range. It is discussed in detail in Chapters 6 and 21.

Playing the ball forward or rearward from the

normal position may be either helpful or detrimental, depending on whether the LA of your particular driver is less or greater than the ideal value for your particular swing.

Figure 8-8 shows this effect. Playing the ball a few inches forward from normal may cause a distance increase of 5 yards or more if your driver has less LA than ideal, or it may even be a loss if your driver has more LA than optimum.

If your driver has optimum LA, playing the ball forward can gain no more than 1 or 2 yards. Also, playing the ball forward or rearward tends to make the ball go left or right, respectively. You must learn to adjust your aim direction by practice with such shots. The complications seem worthwhile mainly for distance champions.

This is a rather different problem for irons as discussed in Chapter 12. More detail regarding Figure 8-8 is given in the Technical Notes below.

Our computerized modeling and optimizing methods replace the trial and error design procedure. This makes it possible for the first time to optimize designs. The model makes it practical to compute graphs such as Figures 8-5, 8-6, 8-7, and 8-8.

There are many other factors, such as face surface shape and face outline shape which strongly affect the scatter of the stop points of each hit. In this chapter we have been concerned with obtaining maximum distance. Later chapters will explain more about accuracy.

The designer's goal for drivers is to obtain maximum distance together with maximum accuracy.

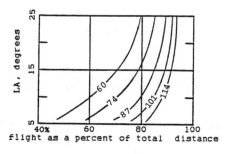

Fig. 8-2 *Effect of LA and HS on the flight distance for drivers. HS is marked on each curve.*

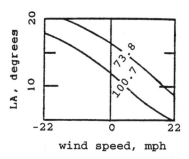

Fig. 8-3 *Optimum LA for drivers depends on the wind speed. Only two HS values are shown, but the trend is clear. Wind speeds which are negative are following wind; positive is for a head wind.*

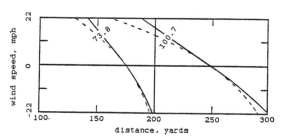

Fig. 8-4 *The effect of wind speed on CHD for drivers. HS is marked on each curve. The dotted curves are for the LA which is optimum at zero wind speed. The solid curves are for an imaginary case where a golfer uses a club with optimum LA for each value of wind speed.*

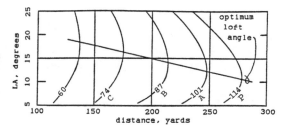

Fig. 8-1 *CHD for a driver versus LA. HS and golfer class are marked on each curve. The curves show that a golfer with low HS might tolerate a driver having about 7 degrees more or less loft than his ideal value without much loss of distance. A strong golfer might tolerate about 2 degrees more or less.*

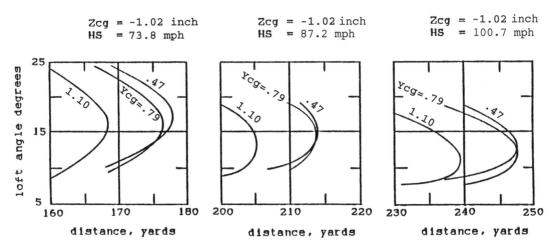

Fig. 8-5 *The effect of Ycg and LA on CHD with Zcg = −1.02 inch, for drivers.*

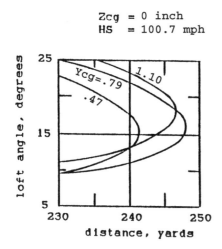

Fig. 8-6 *The effect of Ycg and LA with Zcg = 0, for drivers.*

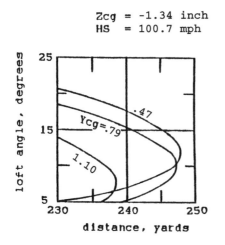

Fig. 8-7 *The effect of Ycg and LA with Zcg = −1.34 inch, for drivers.*

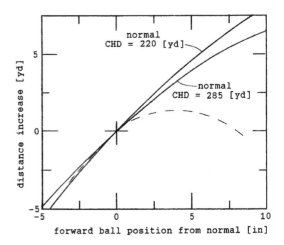

Fig. 8-8 *The effect of playing the ball more forward or back in the stance for drivers. The two solid curves assume that the LA is optimized for each ball position. Several yards can be gained by playing the ball rather far forward if the club has appropriate reduction of LA for each case. The dashed curve shows that if the golfer with normal 285 yard CHD uses LA optimized only for the normal ball position, the distance gain is much smaller and is even a loss if played too far forward.*

Table 8-1 *The LA and Ycg values which give maximum distance for each of the graphs of Figures 8-5, 8-6, and 8-7.*

Figure number	8-5	8-5	8-5	8-6	8-7
HS [mph]	73.8	87.2	100.7	100.7	100.7
Zcg [in]	−1.02	−1.02	−1.02	0	−1.34
Optimum loft angle [deg]	16.48	14.40	12.36	16.47	10.86
Optimum Ycg [in]	.60	.63	.65	.88	.60

TECHNICAL NOTES

Playing the ball farther forward or rearward from the normal stance affects CHD. Figure 8-8 illustrates this effect. The caption explains the graph and the special conditions involved.

An example will help clarify the conditions. For a driver with the optimum LA when the ball is in the normal address position, one would need to use a similar driver but with newly optimized LA (which calculation shows to be about 3 degrees less) to realize the indicated gain by playing the ball 5 inches forward.

The dashed curve shows that playing the ball forward for a golfer who hits 285 yards can cause gain of only 1 or 2 yards if he uses a driver without the change of LA. This further illustrates the effect of using or not using a club designed with the appropriate LA when the ball position is moved.

If the driver does not have ideal LA at normal address position, these curves would be altered considerably. For example, if LA is too high, playing the ball to the rear will gain CHD and playing forward will lose CHD. If LA is too low, playing the ball forward will gain more distance than the curves indicate.

As shown in figure, there is much complication for drivers about gaining or losing CHD when changing address position of the ball.

BALL SPEED, LAUNCH ANGLE, AND BACKSPIN

WITH EVERY HOLE YOU PLAY, YOUR SHOTS PRODUCE A LAUNCH ANGLE, BACKSPIN, AND SIDE SPIN. HERE ARE SOME FACTS ABOUT THEIR EFFECTS. WHEN YOU HAVE AN IRON IN YOUR HANDS, YOU WANT GOOD RESULTS.

Effects of HS, LA, and cg location on distance were illustrated for drivers in Chapter 8. Here, for drivers, we illustrate the effects of LA and spin rate on launch angle, height of the shot, forward distance, and lateral distance for HS = 100.7 mph, golfer A.

Figure 9-1 shows results of impact of a driver head and ball for club HS of 100.7 mph (golfer A); other HS values produce similar curves. These curves are calculated from the model and agree well with golfer experience.

For clubs having small or medium LA values, the launch velocity is considerably higher than the HS of the club. When LA is rather high, launch velocity of the ball becomes equal to, or smaller than HS. As a matter of curiosity, we did calculations showing that LA must be higher than about 47 degrees for this head design for the launch velocity to become smaller than the club HS. This angle where launch velocity equals HS depends only slightly on HS but is rather sensitive to the cg location.

The upper curve of Figure 9-1 also shows that the ball's launch angle is about the same as the club's LA for this particular driver. This curve is a little different for other designs.

The spin rate is also shown in Figure 9-1. As is well known, it increases rapidly when LA increases and when HS increases. This spin rate is commonly called "backspin".

Many believe that backspin can be reduced until it reverses and becomes over spin. Over spin is nearly impossible with any normal golf club, except for balls which are badly topped and do not rise off the ground. If LA is negative as in a very few putters, a very small amount of over spin is possible. What is often thought of as over spin is merely reduced backspin.

What is called "side spin" happens when the golfer has an open or closed club face at impact, relative to the direction of travel of the clubhead. In backspin, the ball rotates around a horizontal axis. If there is a component of side spin for the ball, this axis is tilted out of horizontal. Side spin is negligible for center hits when the club face is square to the line of travel of the clubhead at impact. Side spin is the cause of slices and hooks when cross wind is negligible. Chapters 3 and 25 give more information about hooks and slices. A small amount of side spin doesn't affect forward distance much, but it can cause large lateral errors.

As golfers know, backspin is also helpful when a shot lands on a green, because it helps make the ball stay close to where it lands or even to back up.

In the absence of wind, side spin is always present when a shot curves (fades or draws), tending to reduce total distance; side spin is never present on straight shots.

Calculation, and the experience of golfers, show that lateral errors caused by side spin are a smaller percent of the drive distance for golfers with a slow HS. This probably accounts for some of the truth in the saying that old timers hit right down the center of the fairway. It also explains much of the trouble that goes with long hits made by golfers with high HCP.

SYMBOLS AND DEFINITIONS	
cg [] center of gravity (more accurately, center of mass); its location is usually given in inches.	inches, HW = 200 grams, and 43.5 gram grip which we used in golfer tests and for frequent reference. Notice that modern drivers usually give 5 to 10 yards greater CHD than this reference.
CHD [yd] center hit distance.*	
golfer A a representative golfer with CHD = 251 yards and HS = 100.7 mph on our Reference T driver and with HCP = 10.	**ZBR** [yd] bounce and roll distance for clubs other than putters, measured from where the ball hits down and the flight (carry) ends.*
HS [mph] head speed, speed of the cg of the head just prior to impact.	
LA [deg] loft angle.*	* More detail will be found for these items in the Appendix.
reference T driver a driver with 88 gram graphite shaft, CLG = 43	

They often hook or slice off the fairway.

Most golfers believe that side spin causes far greater lateral errors when driving into a strong head wind. Calculations show that it does cause somewhat larger lateral errors, but not much. Head wind greatly diminishes distance which causes a lateral error to appear larger because it is a much larger fraction of the drive distance.

The Technical Notes give more detail about effects of backspin and side spin for those who may be interested.

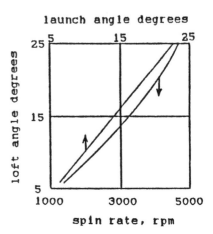

Fig. 9-1 *Launch conditions for golfer A using a typical driver, launch angle at the top and spin rate at the bottom. Notice that the arrows show whether to read the upper or lower scale.*

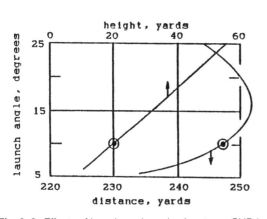 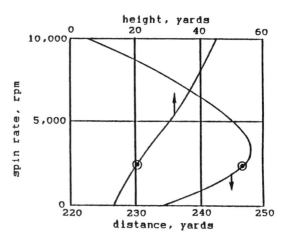

Fig. 9-2 *Effects of launch angle and spin rate on CHD including ZBR and height of the shot. This is for golfer A. Notice that the arrows show whether to read the upper or lower scale. The circles represent a typical driver with 10 degrees LA. On the right, LA is constant at 10 degrees.*

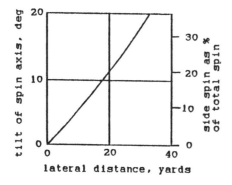

Fig. 9-3 *Effect of side spin for golfer A. Either the left or right scale may be used as a measure of side spin.*

TECHNICAL NOTES

Figure 9-2 has 2 graphs which are examples of the distance and height of the trajectory. The left graph shows launch angle (not LA) effects and the right graph shows ball spin rate effects. All curves are for constant launch velocity of 142.9 mph which corresponds to the encircled points for HS of 100.7 mph.

For the left graph, increasing launch angle causes CHD to increase steadily up to a maximum of about 260 yards at launch angle of about 16 degrees, then CHD diminishes. The encircled point is somewhat below the maximum CHD for this example.

The right graph shows how spin rate (mainly caused by LA and HS) affects height. Notice that this graph is only for illustrating effects of spin with no other changes. The graph also shows that too much spin reduces the distance. This is because more spin causes a small increase of aerodynamic drag, more aerodynamic lift, and therefore the ball slows more rapidly and has higher flight. The flight may even curve upward for high spin combined with high ball speed.

The optimum amount of backspin gives maximum flight distance because it gives the best balance among these effects. It reduces the bounce and roll distance (ZBR), but makes up for this by more flight distance, often called carry distance.

Figure 9-3 shows lateral distance caused by side spin for golfer A with a driver. If golfers want straight shots, this lateral distance is an error. Two different ways to measure side spin are used in the graph. One measure is the side spin rate and the other measure is the tilt of the spin axis. The lateral distance is nearly proportional to the amount of side spin.

FULL SHOTS WITH IRONS AND WOODS

T HE BASIC BEHAVIOR OF IRON SHOTS FOR VARIOUS GOLFERS WHO ARE LONG HITTERS OR SHORT.

INTRODUCTION

Expert golfers know the behavior of each of their clubs. Average golfers have a less clear understanding. This chapter gives results of our model for various clubs including graphs of ZBR.

This chapter only examines full swings with irons that are good center hits and land on the green, and for woods which land on the fairway. Iron shots which don't land on the green usually have smaller ZBR.

Tests with golfers on real shots give a good understanding of the shots but tests usually can't reveal the effects of small changes. Speed of the green (Stimp readings) are important but even for constant Stimp, the greens are never the same where every shot lands and ZBR varies considerably.

Wind, weather, and the kind of ball used also affect results. Results from our model have no such disturbances. These results may not exactly match

you and your golf course but they will show trends and give good comparisons of the irons for golfers of various swing speeds in average conditions.

We found HS for each club and golfer class according to our methods described in Chapter 2.

CHD depends strongly on LA and much less on other design features. We studied old-style irons which are representative of irons popular about 1980 ("traditional irons") and also more modern irons. Modern irons differ mainly by having lower LA and often, larger heads. Club length (CLG) and head weight (HW) have changed only a little.

Here in Chapter 10, we consider the case of no wind at sea level and good greens with Stimp readings of 10 feet and assume the greens are reasonably flat and tipped slightly toward the fairway. (Chapter 11 considers partial swings.)

HCP is important for calculations such as accuracy, but here we are only concerned with center hits, so HCP is not a factor.

Table 10-1 and Figure 10-1 show the results. They are for a traditional set of irons. Figure 10-1 agrees well with experience of golfers who are near golfer A's ability. The curves for golfer P are quite similar to those in Figure 10-1 but the ball climbs faster in the early part of the flight and flies higher and farther with smaller ZBR. Golfers B and C are similar but their shots fly lower and not as far and have larger ZBR.

HEIGHT

If you need to hit over trees or other obstacles, you may not always know which iron will give the highest flight and where in the trajectory the maximum height is reached. This section will help you.

The modern trend has been to use lower loft angles so that a modern club is similar to a traditional

SYMBOLS AND DEFINITIONS	
CHD [yd] center hit distance.*	tests and for frequent reference. Notice that modern drivers usually give up to 5 yards greater CHD than this reference.
CLG [in] club length.*	
golfer P a representative golfer with CHD=281 yards and HS=114.1 mph on our Reference T driver and with HCP=0.	
	HCP handicap.
	HS [mph] head speed, speed of the cg of the head just prior to impact.
golfer A a representative golfer with CHD=251 yards and HS=100.7 mph on our Reference T driver and with HCP=10.	**HW** [gm] head weight (mass), weight of the head without shaft.
	LA [deg] loft angle.*
golfer B a representative golfer with CHD=217 yards and HS=87.2 mph on our Reference T driver and with HCP=20.	**LAE** [deg] effective LA, somewhat different from LA because centrifugal force bends the shaft and at impact, somewhat changes clubhead orientation; head rotation also affects LAE.
golfer C a representative golfer with CHD=179 yards and HS=73.8 mph on our Reference T driver and with HCP=27.5.	**ZBR** [yd] bounce and roll distance for clubs other than putters, measured from where the ball hits down and the flight (carry) ends.*
reference T driver a driver with 88 gram graphite shaft, CLG=43 inches, HW=200 grams, and 43.5 gram grip which we used in golfer	* More detail will be found for these items in the Appendix.

club about one club number lower. For example, many modern 7 irons are about the same as a traditional 6 iron. This is not a design improvement, but merely a change in labeling.

There are several particularly interesting things in Figure 10-1 and Table 10-1. The 6 or 7 iron gives the highest flight of all of the clubs. Many golfers will be surprised to see that the irons with highest loft do not give the highest flight. Their lower ball launch velocity is the reason. The driver gives shots which are only about 60% as high as the 6 or 7 iron (7 or 8 iron in the case of modern irons).

In all cases, the highest point in a shot is reached at a distance which is 50% to 60% of the total distance (more for higher HS and less for lower HS). This will help you to judge whether or not you can hit over a tree. You must be more concerned with the tree's height if it is a little farther than 50% or 60% of the shot distance or is much less.

We measure ZBR from where the ball first hits the ground to where it stops. When the ball backs up, most observers judge the back up distance as the distance from its farthest position. That is not the entire ZBR. You can understand this better if you realize that the ball always bounces forward except in an extreme head wind, but after the bounce stops, it may move either forward or backward. Our ZBR is the result of the forward bounce and the forward or backward movement which follows.

Bounce and Roll Distance

For any given club with a full swing, ZBR for short hits (low HS) is larger than for long hits, confirming the experience of golfers. For example, compare the 9-iron results in Table 10-1 for the different golfers. ZBR is .2 yard for golfer P, .7 yard for golfer A, 1.9 yards for golfer B and 4.2 yards for golfer C. With a partial swing, ZBR increases until the swing is very short as you will see in the next chapter.

Table 10-1 illustrates a disadvantage for golfers with low head speeds (short hitters). When they hit the green, especially with longer irons, they have long ZBR. For example, golfer P with a 3 iron has ZBR of only 4.7 yards, but golfer C has ZBR of 23.2 yards.

ZBR is a major source of variation because it depends strongly on whether the soil is hard or soft at the point where the ball hits. This changes from one golf course to another and it depends on how short and how recently the grass was cut, and how recently it was watered.

Slope at the point of landing has a large effect, which we have not modeled. It could be modeled if desired, with the complication of a number of additional variables.

Discussion

Results for individual golfers will be affected in a number of ways. For example, the distance will be affected if the golfer does not have the average stance which we have modeled, especially if the ball is played farther forward or back in stance. Also, individual golfers may have their hands more forward or rearward at the instant of impact than the average, thus altering the effective loft angle, LAE.

These calculations are especially good for comparisons for various conditions. Your experience may be somewhat different from the calculations, but most trends will be similar.

Such comparisons are much easier to calculate than to measure because of the experimental variations which we described above. Most of the usual discussions of golf club performance are based on extensive experience and close observation. Because our discussions are based on calculations, they are reasonably accurate and especially, they are almost perfectly repeatable and readily show the result of small changes.

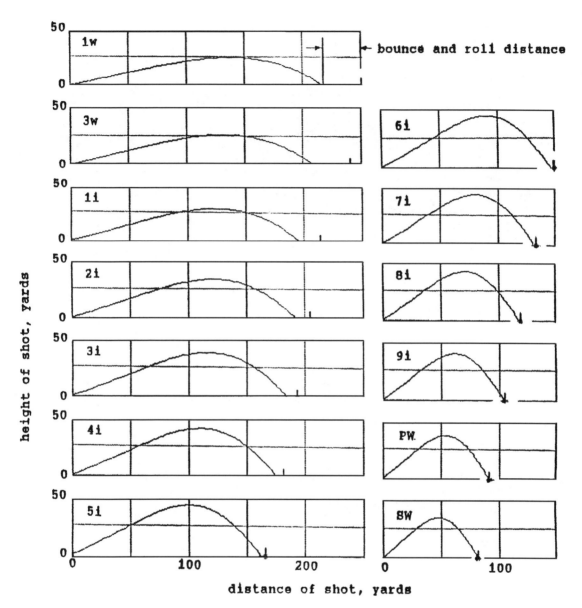

Fig. 10-1 *Comparison of center hits which land and stop on flat greens for golfer A with traditional irons. Two woods are included, showing shots landing on a fairway. Golfers P, B, and C are similar but longer and higher for P and shorter and lower for B and C. Refer to Table 10-1 and to the text for more detail.*

Table 10-1 *Characteristics of center hits which land and stop on flat greens for golfers P, A, B, and C with traditional irons. Two woods are included. Modern irons have lower LA and are similar except about one club number lower. For example, a modern 7 iron is more like the traditional 6 iron in this table. Figure 10-1 shows golfer A graphically.*

club number	golfer P				golfer A				golfer B				golfer C			
	height yards	flight yards	bounce and roll yards	total distance yards	height yards	flight yards	bounce and roll yards	total distance yards	height yards	flight yards	bounce and roll yards	total distance yards	height yards	flight yards	bounce and roll yards	total distance yards
1w	35.6	254.0	26.9	280.9	24.5	218.3	32.5	250.8	16.0	178.5	38.5	217.0	9.7	134.9	44.2	179.1
3w	36.8	241.9	25.5	267.4	26.3	210.5	30.3	240.8	17.2	171.1	36.0	207.1	10.3	127.4	41.2	168.6
1i	40.0	225.0	10.5	235.5	28.5	197.1	16.9	214.0	18.7	161.8	26.1	187.9	11.3	121.4	37.4	158.8
2i	45.9	216.3	6.9	223.2	33.4	192.4	11.8	204.2	22.5	161.8	19.3	181.1	14.0	123.6	29.6	153.2
3i	50.4	205.2	4.7	209.9	37.3	184.8	8.3	193.1	25.7	157.1	14.5	171.6	16.4	122.9	23.2	146.1
4i	53.2	192.9	3.4	196.3	40.0	175.3	6.2	181.5	28.0	150.7	11.1	161.8	18.2	119.5	18.6	138.1
5i	55.5	176.0	2.2	178.2	42.3	161.5	4.1	165.6	30.3	140.5	7.8	148.3	20.1	113.2	13.8	127.0
6i	56.2	158.9	1.3	160.2	43.4	146.8	2.7	149.4	31.6	128.8	5.5	134.3	21.4	105.0	10.2	115.2
7i	55.2	142.1	.7	143.4	43.1	131.8	1.7	133.5	31.8	116.3	3.8	120.1	21.9	95.5	7.5	103.0
8i	52.9	126.6	.4	127.0	41.6	117.4	1.1	118.5	31.0	103.8	2.7	106.5	21.3	85.6	5.6	91.2
9i	49.6	112.2	.2	112.4	39.2	103.9	.7	104.6	29.5	91.7	1.9	93.6	20.8	75.7	4.2	79.9
PW	46.0	99.0	.0	99.0	36.5	91.3	.3	91.6	27.7	80.5	1.2	81.7	19.7	66.4	3.0	69.4
SW	42.8	88.6	-.1	88.5	34.2	81.5	.2	81.7	26.1	71.7	.8	72.5	18.7	59.2	2.1	61.3

PARTIAL SHOTS WITH IRONS

OH! THOSE LOW SHOTS INTO THE WIND; THE NEED TO CLEAR A TREE; THE EUROPEAN BOUNCE AND ROLL SHOTS. LEARN ABOUT THE BEHAVIOR OF YOUR IRONS.

Short shots are important, especially when using a short iron. Common procedure is to use the appropriate iron with a full swing until the distance is less than a full shot with the shortest iron. Head speed (HS) for full swings is widely believed to be controlled better than HS for partial swings. This seems reasonable, but we have made no attempt to compare HS variations for full and partial swings by experiments with golfers. Such tests would be interesting and useful, given a good head speed indicator and a number of golfers as subjects. Very short shots (chip shots) are further discussed in Chapter 23.

Many golfers are not sure what happens when they choose some club other than the one they usually use for partial swings. In this chapter, graphs show the results of partial swings with various short irons, putting partial swings on a quantitative basis. These results should help you with your club choice.

It is very difficult to collect this information by systematic tests with real golfers on real golf courses but our computer modeling makes it easy to do a complete exploration. So, our purpose is to increase what you may already know about how short irons work for short shots with partial swings.

Figure 11-1 shows what HS is needed for the distance desired with the various short irons. This figure is a guide for the HS values needed to interpret the other figures. The process is to estimate the CHD you need and locate that on the vertical scale of

Figure 11-1. Go horizontally to the curve for the iron you intend to use and from this point, go straight down to find the needed HS.

All of these figures are for modern oversize irons, using a Dunlop Maxfli DDhII ball on level greens with Stimp 10. Other clubs, balls, green slope, Stimp, or golfer characteristics will cause similar trends when one club is compared with another and when the effects of one variable are compared with another.

Differences will be approximately as expected as conditions change. For example Stimp and slope will change ZBR. These graphs are independent of golfer skill; remember they apply only to center hits.

After you have estimated the needed HS by this process, you can use this HS number with the other graphs in Figures 11-2, 3, 4, and 5. These figures show respectively, flight distance, ZBR, maximum height, and distance at which maximum height is reached. In these graphs, only good center hits are considered with partial swings.

For very short hits, such as 5 or 10 yards, the flight distance rapidly becomes small and most of the distance is then in ZBR.

Figure 11-3 shows that using the wedges will minimize ZBR. ZBR can be a large source of variation caused by factors independent of club choice (slope, Stimp, etc.) which are reduced by a small ZBR such as is provided by a wedge.

A problem here is that a highly lofted wedge, such as a 60-degree wedge, is harder to hit because there is smaller tolerance for up and down errors. Chapter 24 explains the up-down hitting problems in detail. Therefore, many golfers will have better results with their SW, PW or a 9-iron even though ZBR is larger.

Usually, you would not be concerned with height for partial swings, but sometimes there is a

SYMBOLS AND DEFINITIONS	
CHD [yd] center hit distance.*	**ZBR** [yd] bounce and roll distance for
HS [mph] head speed, speed of the cg	clubs other than putters, meas-
of the head just prior to impact	ured from where the ball hits
PW pitching wedge.	down and the flight (carry) ends.
Stimp [ft] speed of the green, 9 ft being	See PD for putt distance.
typical, (often abbreviated as S).*	* More detail will be found for these items in
SW sand wedge.	the Appendix.

bush or tree which you must clear. Our calculations show some simple approximations to guide you:

Maximum height for a 6 or 7 iron is about 17% of the expected flight distance for shots shorter than about 40 yards and increases to 50% or 60% for full shots. For PW and SW with shots shorter than 40 yards, height is greater, up to about 25% of flight distance. Maximum height is reached at about half the expected flight distance.

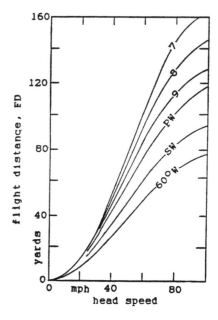

Fig. 11-2 *Flight distance for partial swings.*

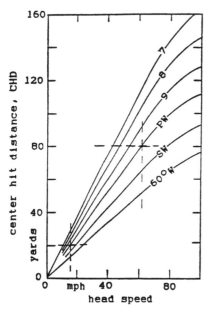

Fig. 11-1 *CHD for partial swings. For example for 80 yards with PW, you need HS=62 mph. Use this figure to find HS for use with the other figures.*

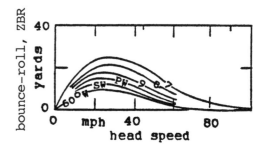

Fig. 11-3 *ZBR (bounce and roll distance) for partial swings.*

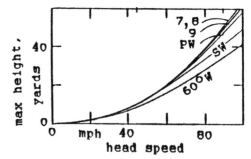

Fig. 11-4 *Maximum height for partial swings.*

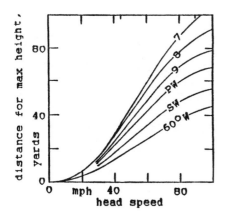

Fig. 11-5 *Distance at which maximum height is reached for partial swings.*

Our model reveals the rather complicated interrelation among flight distance, ZBR, maximum height, and distance at which maximum height is reached. Figures 11-2 through 11-5 give this detail. (Chapter 10 gives this information for full shots.)

It is interesting that Figure 11-4 shows that the 7-, 8-, 9-iron, and PW give height results which depend on head speed but do not vary much from one club to another. For distances less than about 20 yards, even the sand wedge and the 60-degree wedge also give about the same height for a given HS, but of course, distance varies among these clubs as shown in the example below.

Figure 11-4 (which seems to suggest that SW goes the same or a little lower than, say, a 7-iron) is an example of the complication. Consider HS = 40 mph. Figure 11-4 shows that for this case, the 7-iron goes about the same height as the SW. The important thing is that for this example, the 7-iron goes about 75 yards and the SW goes only about 40 yards. When Figure 11-1 is used for the same distance, say, 40 yards, then HS is only about 21 mph for the 7-iron and 40 for the SW; and the respective heights are about 2 yards and 10 yards. Comparisons should be done in a similar way for the other graphs.

IRON SHOTS WHEN THE BALL POSITION IS MOVED BACK

WHEN YOU PLAY THE BALL BACK IN YOUR STANCE WITH VARIOUS IRONS, WHAT HAPPENS? READ ON.

Most golfers know what distance they get for full shots with each iron when they play the ball in its normal position. In deep grass or other special conditions, they may prefer to position the ball farther back at address. They know that this will give more distance if deep grass doesn't slow the clubhead too much.

Many golfers are not sure how much more distance they will get even if the grass doesn't slow the clubhead. It depends mainly on HS, LA for the club, and how far back they position the ball. They may also want to make a very low shot with longer irons because of wind or some overhanging obstruction such as tree branches.

Our model copes with the variable of ball position and the results are our subject for this chapter. We have put the results in a form which makes it easy to estimate how much extra distance will be gained.

This chapter is mainly about bCHD, the increase in center hit distance when the ball is moved back with no change in HS or other inputs.

For all golfers with a given head speed, we found that when they use full swings, bCHD is about the same for the short irons including the 7, 8, 9, PW, and SW. Also, we found that bCHD is approximately proportional to the distance by which they move the ball back from its normal position. Golfers with higher head speed get larger bCHD.

We were able to show bCHD in a single graph, as a fairly good approximation for full swings of all golfer classes, but only for the shorter irons. Figure 12-1 gives this result.

To use it, find the CHD for your driver on the bottom scale if you use a traditional driver length (42 to 44 inch), or on the top scale if you use a modern long-shaft driver. (While the graph doesn't refer to a driver, the CHD for a driver is a guide for the HS in this figure for the other clubs and shows how a strong hitter gets a larger effect.) For example, look at the dotted lines on Figure 12-1. In one case, where the CHD is 190 yards, notice where the dashed line crosses the curve; the bCHD per inch of backward movement of the ball, shown on the left scale of the graph, is 1 yard per inch. In the other example, where CHD is 275 yards, bCHD (where the curves meets the dashed line) is about 1.7 yards per inch.

This number is the approximate number of yards you may expect to gain using a full swing for each inch by which you move the ball back from its normal position.

Thus, in the second example, if you play the ball back a full 5 inches, you would expect to gain 8.5 yards, or 5 times 1.7 yards.

Note that when grass or water slows your clubhead for a normal ball position, results may be much different when the ball is moved back. There is less or no slowing effect on your clubhead when the ball is moved back, usually giving more distance.

Figure 12-1 is an approximation. Therefore, it is reasonable to estimate only to the nearest tenth of a yard per inch. It assumes full swings and your ball

---

SYMBOLS AND DEFINITIONS

bCHD [yd] the increase of CHD when the ball is moved back with no change in HS or other inputs.

CHD [yd] center hit distance.*

golfer P a representative golfer with CHD=281 yards and HS=114.1 mph on our reference T driver and with HCP=0.

golfer A a representative golfer with CHD=251 yards and HS=100.7 mph on our reference T driver and with HCP=10.

golfer B a representative golfer with CHD=217 yards and H=87.2

mph on our reference T driver and with HCP=20.

golfer C a representative golfer with CHD=179 yards and HS=73.8 mph on our reference T driver and with HCP=27.5.

HCP handicap.

HS [mph] head speed, speed of the cg of the head just prior to impact.

LA [deg] loft angle.*

PW pitching wedge.

SW sand wedge.

* More detail will be found for these items in the Appendix.

landing on good, level greens. It also applies only to irons shorter than the 6-iron, and to balls which hit the green and stop on the green. If they stop on the fairway, it is a poorer approximation.

All you need to know to make use of the information in the graph is to remember the number of yards per inch for your particular CHD and remember that this applies only to full swings with irons shorter than the 6-iron. You need not refer to Figure 12-1 again.

Our calculations also showed that the ball is likely to land more to the right than usual when the ball position is moved back. To correct this, aim somewhat to the left provided you square your club-head as if the ball were in its normal position. You may want to rotate your clubhead to a more closed orientation, instead. We believe closing the clubhead is ok, especially if you also aim slightly to the left. It usually gives larger bCHD.

Figure 12-2 shows approximately what to expect when playing balls back for clubs longer than the 7 iron, but it applies only to golfer A. Golfer P will get more gain and golfers B and C will get less.

More details about Figure 12-2 are in the Technical Notes, which also show how we used Figure 12-2 to arrive at Figure 12-1.

Playing the ball back is helpful in some cases such as deep grass because the clubhead travels a smaller distance through the grass before it hits the ball. Some golfers will do this when the ball is partly in the water for the same reason: the head travels through a smaller distance of water.

When the contact position is rather far back, it is nearly the same as using a club with less loft but somewhat different because it uses a descending blow. Playing the ball a large distance back gives the advantage that a golfer has more tolerance for up-down hits (detail about up-down tolerance is in Chapter 24). That makes it easier to hit clubs with very high LA (such as the 60-degree wedge). Of course, it will also cause much larger divots and may even cause the club to stop in the turf if the ball position is very far back.

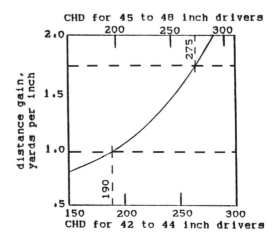

Fig. 12-1 *This is a guide for estimating your distance gain for moving the ball back. It applies only to irons shorter than the 6 iron. Use the top or bottom CHD which suits your driver. See text for more detail. The dashed lines give 2 examples.*

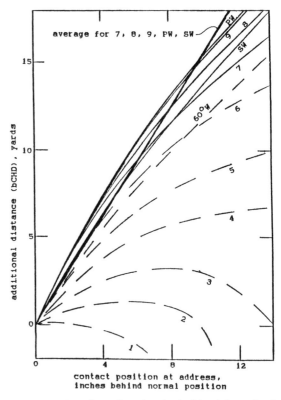

Fig. 12-2 *The effect of moving the ball back for golfer A. This applies only for irons. The longer irons do not gain much distance. Figure 12-1 is a guide for the short irons for this and other golfer classes.*

TECHNICAL NOTES

Figure 12-2 is for all of the irons for golfer A. The heavy line is a reasonable average for the short irons (7, 8, 9, PW, and SW). The curves for the other clubs have much smaller bCHD and they are quite different from one another. They show that playing the ball back more than a few inches can be quite detrimental for the longest irons. This agrees with what most golfers would expect.

We studied all 4 golfer classes. We found that the same clubs grouped together about as well as for golfer A in Figure 12-2. For golfer C, the 60-degree wedge also was part of the group, but not for the other classes. We found the corresponding heavy line for each golfer class, which allowed us to calculate the results given in Figure 12-1. Figure 12-1 is a reasonably good approximation for all of the various golfer classes (A, B, and C).

If a golfer wants to make a low shot by moving the ball rather far back with the longer irons, a full swing can still give good distance but may be very unpleasant if the clubhead stops in the turf. We have not analyzed the effect of moving the ball back for partial swings.

GREENS ABOVE OR BELOW THE GOLFER

Golfers never forget hitting balls to greens that are very high or very low. An off-center hit may ruin your entire day. There are ways to handle this phenomenon.

Often, the golfer faces elevated or depressed greens. On your home course, you usually know by experience which club to use. This chapter will help you make the right choice of clubs on unfamiliar courses. These results are for flat, level greens at Stimp 10 feet.

The flight distance is less when the green is higher and more when lower. In most cases, ZBR is small and does not change greatly. There is a simple, easy-to-remember rule for guidance described below.

Figure 13-1 shows the nature of full shots to elevated and depressed greens for golfer A with a 7-iron. Other irons are rather similar but shots are longer for golfer P and shorter for B, and C.

The figure shows only small changes in ZBR. If the green is nearly as high as the high point in the flight, then the ball descends only a small distance before it makes impact and ZBR is rather large, but such cases are less common. Figure 13-1 also shows that the downward angle of travel of the ball as it lands changes little between the case of an elevated green and the case of a depressed green. Flight distance is the principal variation.

Other irons have similar effects, but longer irons affect golfer B and C more than P and A because B and C have lower shots.

Figure 13-2 supplements Figure 13-1 and gives guidance on how to choose the proper iron for elevated or depressed greens. Either vertical scale may be used. The left scale is for LA and the right is for modern irons with strong lofts which compare with traditional irons about 1 number lower. The caption gives an example of how using the figure will allow a golfer to choose the proper iron. The model shows calculations for modern oversize irons but more traditional irons behave similarly.

Notice that some lines do not extend all the way to the right for golfers B and C. That is because a golfer of that skill level using those particular clubs will require 2 shots to reach the elevated green.

Figure 13-2 leads to a surprising result if the greens are level. Approximately, for all the irons with depressed greens, choosing an iron one step shorter is only appropriate for depression of about 20 yards. This is the height of a 5 or 6 story building, something rarely encountered. The reverse is also true for elevated greens if the maximum height of the shot is well above the level of the green. In contrast, conventional advice is to choose an iron one step shorter or longer if greens are respectively 10 yards lower or higher. We suspect this disagreement is because most elevated greens slope more toward the tee and depressed greens are more nearly level. This causes less ZBR for higher greens and more for depressed greens.

We conclude that for typical greens, the rule of one-step difference for a 10 yard elevation or depression is probably good advice. Our calculations showing one step for 20 yards are probably about right only when high or low greens are level.

A marked exception is when the green is elevated nearly as much as the height of the shot.

SYMBOLS AND DEFINITIONS	
CHD [yd] center hit distance.*	CHD = 179 yards and HS = 73.8 mph on our reference T driver and with HCP = 27.5.
golfer P a representative golfer with CHD = 281 yards and HS = 114.1 mph on our reference T driver and with HCP = 0.	**HCP** handicap.
golfer A a representative golfer with CHD = 251 yards and HS = 100.7 mph on our reference T driver and with HCP = 10.	**HS** [mph] head speed, speed of the cg of the head just prior to impact.
	LA [deg] loft angle.*
	ZBR [yd] bounce and roll distance for clubs other than putters, measured from where the ball hits down and the flight (carry) ends. See PD for putt distance.
golfer B a representative golfer with CHD = 217 yards and H = 87.2 mph on our reference T driver and with HCP = 20.	
golfer C a representative golfer with	* More detail will be found for these items in the Appendix.

Then the ball may have very long roll unless the green slopes strongly toward the fairway. A shorter club will not reach the green and a longer one may not fly high enough, so it may require 2 hits to reach the green.

In high mountains, we observed drives off a mountain top over a high cliff which vividly illustrated a depressed green. For our curiosity, we calculated this case for a driver, with results shown in Figure 13-3. Near the end of its flight, the ball doesn't tend to fall nearly vertically downward. That is because the spin rate is still fairly high, and with the increasing downward speed, causes a forward force on the ball. This is the same effect which makes a very strong drive rise for the first part of its flight. At much more extreme heights, the spin would finally approach zero and this effect would disappear.

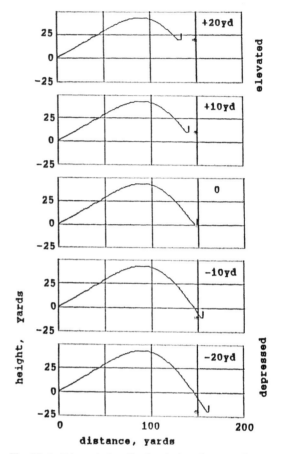

Fig. 13-1 *7 iron shots with elevated or depressed greens for golfer A. Numbers at the right give the green's elevation or depression relative to the golfer. See Figure 13-2 for other clubs and elevations.*

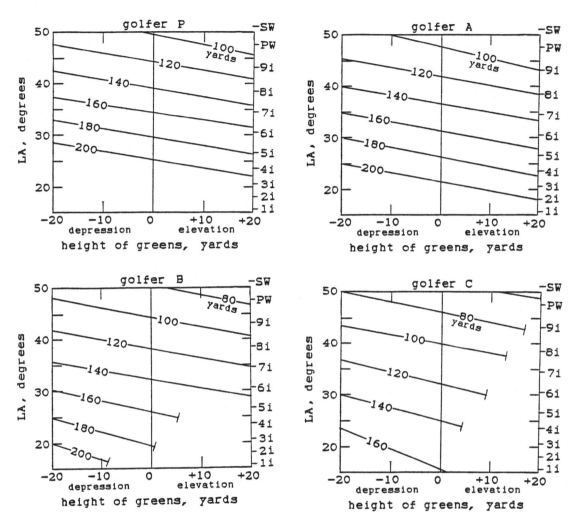

Fig. 13-2 *Selection of irons when the green is depressed or elevated. Use the graph for your golfer class. Find the depression or elevation on the bottom scale and go up to the line which represents the distance needed then right or left to find the club number or LA needed. Example for golfer B: A green about 161 yards away which is depressed 20 yards would need a 6 iron. At zero depression, a 5 iron is about right. Refer to the text for important additional detail.*

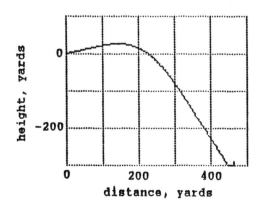

Fig. 13-3 *Driving a ball from a high cliff, as for an extremely depressed green.*

THE EFFECTS OF WIND ON GOLF SHOTS

IS THIS UP YOUR ALLEY OR NOT? HEAD WINDS, SIDE WINDS, AND TAIL WINDS FOR GOLFERS AND
THEIR CLUBS—AND HOW ANY KIND AFFECTS SCATTER OF STOP POINTS.

Figure 14-1 shows the general nature of the flight of a ball with and without wind. This is for ideal center hits by golfer B having head speed with conventional driver of 87.2 mph and handicap 20. It includes 3 different clubs: a driver, a 5-iron, and a 9-iron. To emphasize the effect of wind, we used an unusually large wind speed of 30 mph blowing toward the golfer at 45 degrees. Golfers rarely play in such strong winds.

In Figure 14-1, notice the legend at the right. It shows which are top views of the shot and which are side views (plan views and elevations views). The legend at the left shows which are the graphs for condition of no wind and which are the graphs with 30 mph wind. The top views with no wind are straight lines. With wind, they are strongly curved. The side views show that this wind condition increases the height and shortens the shots.

One surprising result is that the loss of distance

for all 3 clubs is about the same. One reason is that the time of flight does not change greatly from one club to another. The detailed reasons are very complex. Other cases give different results, as will be shown.

Another surprise (to some of us) is that the lateral error is about the same for all 3 clubs. Again, the detailed reasons are quite complex.

The component of the wind toward the golfer causes the ball to fly somewhat higher than with no wind. This is a smaller effect for drivers and larger for the short irons. This is because wind increases lift caused by the ball spin. These shots actually rise a little more steeply as they fly for about the first half of their distance. This can be seen in the lower views. This "climbing" effect is considerably greater for strong hitters. It does not show up for slower swings even with head wind.

Figure 14-2 shows stop points for 500 hits for golfer B with a rather strong wind of 20 mph coming from each of 4 directions as indicated by the 4 arrows. Each circle shows a single perfect center hit where the golfer has none of his usual errors. The small circles are for golfer C, the larger ones are for golfer B, and the largest ones are for golfer A.

Scatter of stop points for golfers A and C are not shown, but would be similar except being smaller and larger, respectively.

The scatter of these 500 points is caused by the golfer's errors. We selected points to be normally distributed from the mean of each of the 5 largest golfer's errors in calculating these stop points. These 5 errors are standard deviations of head speed (dHS), alignment angle (dAA), long axis of hit pattern (dLA), wrist angle (dWA), and short axis of hit pattern (dSA). Errors are discussed in detail in Chapters 4 and 5.

The 3 circles in Figure 14-2 with wind toward

SYMBOLS AND DEFINITIONS	
AA [deg] alignment angle.*	**golfer P** a representative golfer with CHD=281 yards and HS=114.1 mph on our reference T driver and with HCP=0.
CHD [yd] center hit distance. More in Appendix 1.*	
dAA [deg] standard deviation of AA	
dHS [%] standard deviation of HS just before impact as a percent of HS.	**golfer A** a representative golfer with CHD=251 yards and H=100.7 mph on our reference T driver and with HCP=10.
dLA [in] standard deviation of the center of impact locations (hit patterns) on the club face, measured in the direction of the long axis of the impact pattern. dLA is approximately in the toe-heel direction.	**golfer B** a representative golfer with CHD=217 yards and HS=87.2 mph on our reference T driver and with HC=20.
dSA [in] the same as dLA but measured in the direction of the short axis of the hit pattern and is approximately in the up-down direction.	**golfer C** a representative golfer with CHD=179 yards and HS=73.8 mph on our reference T driver and with HCP=27.5.
	HCP handicap.
dWA [deg] for a golfer, the standard deviation of the rotation about the shaft axis from its mean value.*	**HS** [mph] head speed, speed of the cg of the head just prior to impact.*
	* More detail will be found for these items in the Appendix.

the golfer happen to cluster together more than for the other wind directions. This somewhat surprised us. The head wind can reduce the distance for hits with high head speed so much that the ball may actually stop with the same or less distance than for a low head speed.

To explore this further, we calculated Table 14-1 to show center hit distances (CHD) for a variety of cases. It shows that this effect varies greatly with HS, wind speed, and the club being used. The HS values in the table cover a wide range, but do not correspond exactly with any of our usual golfer classes. The 3 circles in Figure 14-2 show only a small part of the whole effect.

It may be concluded that head wind affects CHD proportionately more for strong hitters than for short hitters for drivers; and for the more lofted clubs, the effect is much greater. That is, for the more lofted clubs (shorter clubs), strong hitters must be much more concerned with head wind than short hitters.

This is partly because wind speed increases with height which causes larger effects for high shots, and partly because backspin is higher and considerably alters the flight, reducing the bounce and roll distance, or even reversing it for the shorter clubs. Figure 3-4 in Chapter 3 shows an even more extreme case. You might want to try this when you happen to be on a driving range with a strong headwind, using a sand wedge or a super wedge and a full swing.

These examples are for normal wind conditions with no nearby hills, trees, or buildings. Such things can alter results considerably and golfers must learn to estimate their effects.

Obstructions to the right or left of the fairway generally reduce the effects of cross winds.

It is rather surprising that cross winds give about the same amount of lateral displacement of stop points for short clubs and long clubs. Strong hits indicated by the large circles suffer larger effects than for the small circles, both for side winds and for winds toward or away from the golfer.

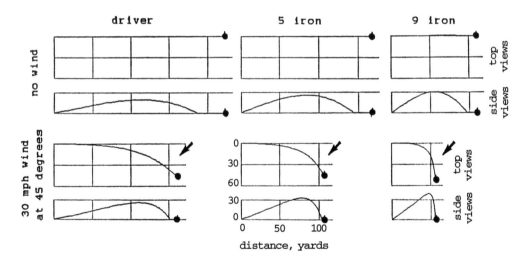

Fig. 14-1 *The general effect of wind on the trajectory of golf shots for golfer B. The upper pairs are under normal conditions with no wind. The lower pairs are for a strong wind of 30 mph blowing toward the golfer at 45 degrees (note arrow). The scale numbers are on one set of graphs, but they apply to all.*

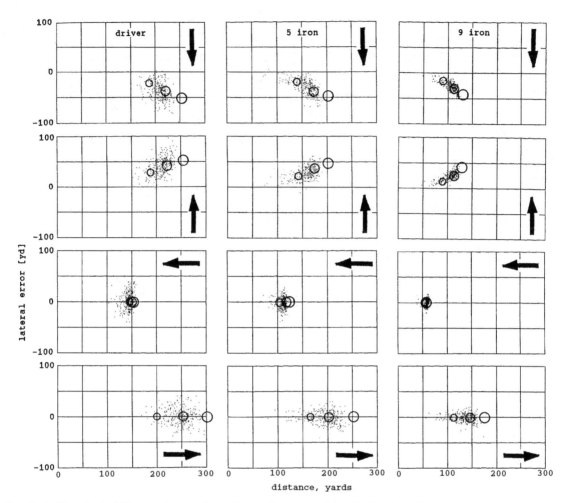

Fig. 14-2 *The effect of 20 mph wind on stop points on the fairway for golfer B with a driver, 5 iron, and 9 iron. Arrows show wind direction. The large circles are center hits for golfer A, the medium circles are for golfer B, and the small circles are for golfer C.*

Table 14-1 *Effect of head wind speed on center hit distance for various clubs and various head speeds. Each 1-wood has optimum LA; other clubs use typical fixed values for LA.*

club	HS	LA	center hit distance, yd head wind speed, mph			
			0	10	20	30
1-wood	50	20.8	103.9	98.0	89.2	76.0
1-wood	70	18.4	162.7	147.9	126.0	95.2
1-wood	90	15.1	217.9	191.4	155.5	109.8
1-wood	110	12.2	264.5	227.1	180.0	135.4
1-wood	130	9.9	302.3	256.0	201.0	156.2
5-iron	40	26.5	86.2	80.7	71.2	56.9
5-iron	60	26.5	129.8	113.7	92.4	68.9
5-iron	80	26.5	170.3	140.0	103.2	54.5
5-iron	100	26.5	198.2	151.3	94.0	23.7
5-iron	120	26.5	212.7	149.8	76.0	-20.6
9-iron	30	43.0	67.1	56.5	44.0	30.5
9-iron	50	43.0	70.6	60.3	48.1	31.4
9-iron	70	43.0	98.4	78.3	50.0	9.0
9-iron	90	43.0	116.8	81.7	34.9	-31.7
9-iron	110	43.0	124.8	75.5	22.2	-72.0

TECHNICAL NOTES

Wind speed normally increases slowly as the distance above the ground increases. Our wind speed numbers refer to a height of 6 feet above the ground. Our computer modeling includes the effects of wind speed increase above the ground. Following Reference 8, the wind speed can be expressed as follows, where V is the wind velocity, h is the height, and Vr is the velocity at reference height hr:

$$V/Vr = (h/hr)^{(1/6)} \; [].$$

ESTIMATING WIND SPEED AND CORRECTING FOR IT

WHEN THE WIND DOES BLOW, CAN YOU ESTIMATE IT? WHAT ARE THOSE BLADES OF GRASS TELLING YOU? SOME PRACTICAL GUIDANCE WILL SOLVE MANY MYSTERIES.

WIND SPEED

Golfers know they must make corrections when the wind is blowing; adjustments needed can become rather large when the wind is strong. In this chapter we suggest rules of thumb for approximate corrections golfers must make for various wind speeds and directions. We will also discuss various methods you can use to estimate wind speed.

With computer modeling, the effects of wind on golf shots can be calculated in great detail and with good accuracy. These details require numerous tables or graphs and are too complicated to be useful and interesting to most golfers, so we have omitted them and simplified the results. Most of this is well known, but we will discuss it in ways which may be more useful to golfers.

In 1805, the Beaufort Scale of wind speed was devised for the British Royal Navy. It is still a useful classification of wind speed, especially so for golfers because it gives results in numbers, instruments are not needed and it's easy to use. Golfers can rapidly learn the Beaufort Scale or use other ways to estimate wind which we will discuss.

Table 15-1 lists the Beaufort Scale up through Beaufort number 6. No one is likely to play golf when the wind speed is higher. The range of most concern

to golfers is Beaufort scale 2 though 5, light through fresh winds.

The Beaufort scale has its drawbacks, however. It is a good guide for wind speed, but doesn't show direction very well. Also, trees, wind vanes, inland water, and umbrellas are not always available to observe.

Some other methods are okay for wind speed and show direction better. The Beaufort speeds will help you learn the others.

VARIOUS WAYS TO ESTIMATE WIND SPEED AND DIRECTION

1. Beaufort scale. Advantages and disadvantages are described above.

2. Toss grass or leaves in the air. This is the most common way for golfers to estimate wind speed and direction. Golfers merely need to observe which direction the grass moves and how fast and how far it moves. It requires practice to estimate a speed number on the result. It is good for estimating direction.

3. Appearance of the flag on the flagstick. The flag shows direction and gives a good idea of wind speed if it is more than 8 or 10 mph. A difficulty is that a flag is not always visible and it is often too far away to see the direction.

4. How the wind feels to the golfer. This can be very useful, quick, and easy. It is more successful if the golfer watches trees and other things related to the Beaufort speeds and after observing for many times, learns how various Beaufort speeds feel. This requires practice. It is easy to face directly into the wind, to show direction.

5. Use some kind of simple wind indicator. You

SYMBOLS AND DEFINITIONS	
CHD [yd] center hit distance.*	mph on our reference T driver and with HCP = 20.
golfer P a representative golfer with CHD = 281 yards and HS = 114.1 mph on our reference T driver and with HCP = 0.	**golfer C** a representative golfer with CHD = 179 yards and HS = 73.8 mph on our reference T driver and with HCP = 27.5.
golfer A a representative golfer with CHD = 251 yards and HS = 100.7 mph on our reference T driver and with HCP = 10.	**HCP** handicap. **HS** [mph] head speed, speed of the cg of the head just prior to impact.
golfer B a representative golfer with CHD = 217 yards and H = 87.2	* More detail will be found for this item in the Appendix.

can use a ribbon or tie something like some yarn or a golf tee on the end of a slender string about 8 inches long. You can hold up the ribbon or string above your head and toward the wind. You observe how far the tip swings in the wind and which direction. It is necessary to calibrate this, such as with the Beaufort scale in the same way as (4) above.

THE PREFERRED ALTERNATIVE METHOD

We think that (2) or (4) are among the best methods because of simplicity. You can improve your skill at estimating wind speed if you frequently look at the things suggested in Table 15-1 and compare how the wind feels to you or how grass clippings fly in the wind. Either one provides a way to learn to estimate wind speed and direction with sufficient accuracy. Perhaps method 4 is the best method of all, however, because it is simplest after you have learned to relate it to the Beaufort scale. If you use method 4, be sure to face *into* the wind when you judge direction.

It is worth learning things listed in Table 15-1 by frequent practice so you become more skilled at estimating speed in the scales of 2 through 5.

EFFECTS OF OBSTRUCTIONS

The discussion above applies when there are no trees, buildings, or other obstructions near you. The obstructions which affect flight of your ball are mostly those which are toward the target. Obstructions near you do not cause much effect (on the flight of the ball) unless they are close and large.

However, nearby obstructions do cause another problem–they make it hard for you to estimate wind speed and wind direction. The Beaufort scale is helpful in such cases because it refers to trees, leaves and branches which often are the actual obstruction. Trees are often tall enough to be affected only by very large obstructions.

EFFECTS OF HEAD WIND OR
TAIL WIND ON YOUR SHOTS

The following rule is worth memorizing. The wind guideline applies about the same for all irons and for all golfer classes.

In a 5-mph head wind, use an iron one step longer; for a 10-mph head wind, 2 steps; 15- or 20-mph, 3 or 4 steps. Tail winds need shorter irons in somewhat smaller steps.

EFFECTS OF SIDE WINDS ON YOUR SHOTS

When wind is directly to one side or the other, it requires aiming corrections and can reduce distance. It changes with golfer class (because of HS) and changes somewhat with distance to the target. This is a more complicated case than head winds or tail winds.

Consider a wind directly from your right at 10 miles per hour. You must aim somewhat to the right and your ball starts off somewhat to the right. Therefore the wind is not exactly to the right of the line of flight of the ball which means there is a small amount of head wind early in the flight. That causes a little loss of distance.

For the aiming correction, we could consider how many *degrees* to aim toward the right or left. This varies with target distance and with the golfer class. It is easier to judge how many *yards* you should aim to the right or left at the target distance.

We can make a reasonably simple description of the corrections needed, depending on target distance and golfer class. Here is what a golfer should try to remember:

- *For 120 to 200 yards distance with a 10-mph cross wind, golfer A should use a normal club and aim about 20 yards toward the wind, as estimated at the target distance. In a 5-mph wind, the golfer should aim 10 yards toward the wind. In a 20-mph wind, golfer A should aim 40 yards toward the wind and uses about a one-step longer iron.*

- *For an 80-yard target distance, golfer A should aim about 14 yards toward the wind and changes to a longer club only when there's a 20-mph wind.*

- *Golfers of other classes should do the same but the distance they aim toward the wind is multiplied by factors of 1.5 for golfer P, 0.6 for golfer B, and 0.4 for golfer C. For example, golfer C in the above instruction for 120 to 200 yards in 10-mph wind would aim 8 yards toward the wind; in a 5-mph wind, 4 yards toward the wind; and in 20-mph wind, 16 yards toward the wind.*

Wind at intermediate angles involves similar kinds of corrections. Unfortunately, the corrections require much more complicated explanations.

Golfers learn by experience and good golfers learn remarkably well. We hope these suggestions will help golfers who are not confident of how to judge the effects of wind on their shots.

Table 15-1 *Beaufort Scale for Wind (numbers above 6 omitted). By permission. From Merriam-Webster's Collegiate® Dictionary, Tenth Edition© 1999 by Merriam-Webster, Incorporated.*

Beaufort number	name	miles per hour	description
0	calm	<1	Smoke rises vertically.
1	light	2	Direction shown by smoke, but most wind vanes don't move.
2	light	5	Wind felt on face. Leaves rustle. Wind vane moved by wind.
3	gentle	10	Leaves in constant motion. Flags partially extended.
4	moderate	15	Raises dust and loose paper. Small branches move.
5	fresh	21	Small trees sway. Crested waves form on inland waters.
6	strong	27	Large branches in motion. Hard to use umbrella.

TECHNICAL NOTES

We made hundreds of computer runs, varying HS, wind speed, club designs, and golfer error inputs. From these, we condensed the details into the approximate rules as stated.

The detailed results were too voluminous for easy reproduction and study by golfers. The calculations show good agreement with experience of golfers, which is a qualitative confirmation of the accuracy and completeness of our model.

Part Three

SOME SPECIAL EFFECTS

LOSS OF DISTANCE CAUSED BY AIR DRAG ON HEAD AND SHAFT

YOU DON'T NEED TO WORRY ABOUT AIR DRAG ON A LARGE HEAD OR ON THE SHAFT WHEN YOU SWING A LARGE-HEAD DRIVER. IT HARDLY AFFECTS THE DISTANCE YOU GET.

THE AIR DRAG PROBLEM

Recently driver head volumes and corresponding face areas have increased from about 160 cubic centimeters and 3 square inches to 250 and even 300 cc with 4.5 sq in or more. These larger faces have the advantage of fewer POF hits. In addition, these large volumes are conducive to large moments of inertia which reduce the penalty for off-center hits and this makes the sweet spot larger.

These things are great improvements if you are among the less skilled golfers. If you are a highly skilled golfer, these are still worthwhile improvements, because a small improvement for a good golfer tends to be relatively as important as a large improvement for a poor golfer. In other words, when a good golfer can reduce a score by even 1 stroke, this gives an advantage which may be relatively as important as when a poor golfer reduces his or her score by perhaps 2 or 3 strokes.

Large heads, as in modern designs, have more air drag and there is no practical way to significantly streamline them. Air drag reduces HS and therefore

CHD is reduced. There has also been some interest in stiffer shafts having larger diameters. This would also increase air drag and decrease CHD.

It is important to know if this extra air drag causes significant loss of distance. This question is not important for other woods (except the first fairway wood) nor for irons because you can always use a club with less loft if you need more distance. You don't have this option with the driver nor for the first fairway wood.

METHODS OF INVESTIGATION

It is difficult to find the answers by experimental means, because it would be necessary to make a number of different drivers having different head sizes but identical weights. Each must have the proper LA and cg location for the HS of each individual test golfer if the resulting CHD is to be meaningful. Further, each driver would need a different shaft diameter but have no difference in shaft weight. Without all these precautions, it would be impossible to know which variable – a wrong LA or weight or cg location – caused observed changes. Even after (or if) all this could be done, the variations at each golfer's skill level would make it necessary to have many hits in order to get good averages.

Also, a mechanical robot golfer is not very helpful in such testing because it is unlikely to interact with changes in air drag the same way as a human golfer.

Good modeling avoids these problems. A reasonable approximation is far better than no knowledge and is also far better than experiments which are not likely to give accurate results and are likely to suggest the wrong conclusions. Here we summarize air drag effects and more detail is given in the Technical Notes.

SYMBOLS AND DEFINITIONS

cg [] center of gravity (more accurately, center of mass); its location is usually given in inches.
CHD [yd] center hit distance.*
golfer P a representative golfer with CHD=281 yards and HS=114.1 mph on our reference T driver and with HCP=0.
golfer A a representative golfer with CHD=251 yards and HS=100.7 mph on our reference T driver and with HCP=10.
golfer B a representative golfer with CHD=217 yards and H=87.2 mph on our reference T driver and with HCP=20.

golfer C a representative golfer with CHD=179 yards and HS=73.8 mph on our reference T driver and with HCP=27.5.
HS [mph] head speed, speed of the cg of the head just prior to impact.
LA [deg] loft angle.*
POF hits partly off the face hits for those hits near the edge of the face for which more than 25% of the imprint area would be off the face.
reference atmospheric conditions altitude at sea level, 70 degrees F, no wind, and 20% relative humidity.
* *More detail will be found for these items in the Appendix.*

RESULTS

Graphs of the results are Figures 16-1 and 16-2. On each graph are 3 curves, one each for golfer A, golfer B, and golfer C. Notice that the figures give the *additional* loss of CHD when the face area is increased above 3 sq in (20 sq cm) in Figure 16-1 and when the shaft diameter is increased above .335 inch in Figure 16-2.

Accordingly, for example, it shows that large shafts and faces are less detrimental for golfer C than for B or A. The most common shaft diameter is .335 inch.

The graphs show that even a very large face increases the loss of CHD by only .7 to 1 yard compared with a small face. Generally we are concerned with gaining every one-tenth yard of CHD which is possible. Here there is a large reward for a large face because it gives more inertia and there are far fewer POF hits (which will be discussed in detail in Chapter 17). Because of this reward, we believe loss even up to .7 or 1 yard is acceptable. Shaft diameter of .5 inch causes loss of about .5 yard which is probably an acceptable compromise for the added stiffness and strength.

The loss of CHD caused by a combination of both large shaft diameter and large head can be found by simply adding the 2 separate losses together.

CONCLUSIONS

These 2 conclusions are closely related: (1) you need not be concerned about the extra amount of air drag for oversize heads and large tip shafts unless they are much larger than present large heads and tips; and (2) you have little distance to gain from heads which are smaller or that claim to be more streamlined.

Even in the case of extremely large heads, air drag causes loss of distance of no more than about .8 yard. The loss is only a little larger for fast head speeds compared to slow.

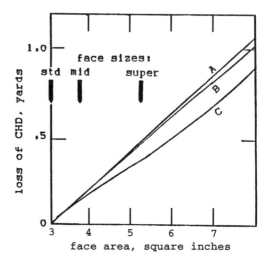

Fig. 16-1 *Loss of CHD for large face drivers relative to CHD for a reference face area of 3 sq in when shaft tip diameter is .335 inch. The curves are for golfers A, B, and C.*

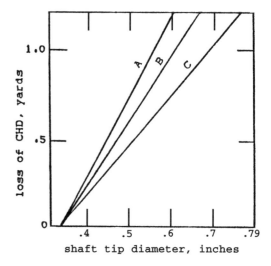

Fig. 16-2 *Loss of a driver's CHD for tip diameters which are large compared to that for a reference shaft diameter of .335 inch when face area is 3 sq in. The curves are for golfers A, B, and C.*

TECHNICAL NOTES

Our analytical procedure started with the relation between HS and time from stroboscopic photos of a swing made with the camera pointing perpendicular to the plane of the swing. From this we could calculate the kinetic energy (KE) of the club just at the bottom of the swing.

We estimated the aerodynamic drag coefficient on the head. Drag area is the important variable, not volume of the clubhead, and we used face area because the face is near to perpendicular to the travel during most of the maximum speed (and maximum drag) part of the swing. For the face, we assumed that when the shaft is horizontal during the downswing, the face is parallel to the air flow and progresses to square at impact. We approximated air drag force as proportional to the flow component normal to the face. To get drag energy loss, we integrated over the component of this force which is in the direction of the head movement.

We changed face area from case to case. From this, we found the energy loss for different head sizes.

We used a similar procedure for the shaft and found drag for a 44-inch shaft having .6 inch butt diameter, with various tip diameters; with a uniform taper from the tip to the butt; and provided for the reduction of air speed at the shaft with distance above the head.

For the shaft, considering an incremental length of shaft and a time increment, the work of aerodynamic drag is the product of the drag force times the distance traveled. This was integrated over the length of the shaft and over the last 90 degrees of the swing to calculate the total work resulting from aerodynamic drag on the shaft.

These integration differences between the face and the shaft are reflected in the somewhat different shapes of the curves in Figures 16-1 and 16-2.

In all cases, head weight and weight of the shaft were held constant at values typical of popular golf clubs.

This gave us the drag energy expended to overcome air drag (DRE). Most of DRE is expended over a fairly short distance before impact, when speeds are highest. In this part of the swing, a golfer can put in little or no more energy. A golfer's total energy input is mostly provided early in the swing and we believe that it is practically constant whether DRE is large or small.

We assigned the name total swing energy (TSE) for the total energy input to the swing by the golfer and assume that TSE doesn't change when DRE changes.

Just before impact, TSE = KE + DRE.

When DRE is zero, we can find KE for no drag, which is TSE. Thus, the values for DRE and TSE give KE when drag is considered. From this value of KE, HS is easily calculated.

The small reduction of HS suggests that there should be slight corresponding changes in LA and cg location for optimum performance. We disregarded this second order effect.

We found that for the reference shaft diameter and reference face area, shaft drag is somewhat greater and causes more loss of head speed and distance than the head drag. This seemed surprising. When we compared the area of the face with the frontal area of the lower one third of the shaft, we found that the shaft area really is comparable or even larger.

The calculations show that even for no air drag, CHD increases only about .5 yard for zero face area and about 1.0 yard for zero shaft area.

In these calculations, guided by Reference 8, we estimated the aerodynamic drag coefficient to be 1.17, based on the face area. Also, for flow perpendicular to the shaft, we estimated the drag coefficient to be 1.20. The calculations were made for "reference atmospheric conditions."

HITS PARTLY OFF THE FACE (POF HITS)

WITH A DRIVER THAT GENERATES THE FASTEST HEAD SPEED, MANY TOP THE BALL OR HIT UNDER IT NOW AND THEN. HERE'S HOW CLUB DESIGN CAN DRASTICALLY REDUCE THE PROBLEM.

We have found no research and design work which specifically considers the effects of hits which are partly off the face (POF hits). Probably, many such hits go unnoticed, which is surprising because it is an important problem for average or lesser-skilled golfers. Good golfers have fewer POF hits, but they do happen and their results would be much better if the problem could be reduced or avoided.

Large face size is seldom emphasized in design of modern large driver heads. Instead, large heads are usually discussed in connection with having large volumes. Almost no attention has been paid to the size of the face or more specifically, to its area and shape.

Taken alone, the volume of a driver head has no significance to club design. It correlates well with highly desirable large moments of inertia, so large head volume tends to be strongly favorable. Large volume does not correlate as closely with large face size.

As you will see in this chapter, we have found that large improvements are possible over present types of driver faces.

We discussed the nature of the distribution of

hits on a golf club face in Chapter 4. Review of Figure 4-2 may be a helpful introduction to the discussion in this chapter.

The distribution of hits allows calculation of the percentage of hits which will be partly off the face, when the face outline and orientation of the club are known. If the face is rather large and has appropriate shape and orientation, the percentage of POF hits may be dramatically reduced, which can be a very important improvement for the golfer.

Figure 17-1 shows when a hit is far enough off the face for us to classify it as a POF hit – when more than 25% of the normal imprint area is off the face. Preliminary investigation indicates that if the imprint is only slightly off the face, it causes little error.

Table 17-1 shows comparisons for golfers with various handicaps (HCP) and percentages of imprint area off the face (AOF) at which an imprint is counted as POF. The various drivers identified in its caption show how strongly the face outline affects the percentage of POF hits, based on a large number of hits.

The large, tilted, elliptical face driver (Driver D) is a preliminary design of our new concept which is discussed in more detail below. It demonstrates the very large improvements which are possible by improving the face size, shape, and orientation.

Notice that the relative ranking of the drivers does not depend on percent of AOF. We arbitrarily chose 25% AOF for design work, as explained in the Technical Notes. The table also vividly shows how much worse the POF problem becomes for the higher HCP golfers.

Our research indicates a definite tendency for low HCP golfers to have higher HS, as would be expected. Handicap affects the size of the hit pattern and HS affects the diameter of the ball imprint on the

SYMBOLS AND DEFINITIONS

CHD [yd] center hit distance.*
drivers A, B, C, D see Table 17-1.
golfer P a representative golfer with CHD=281 yards and HS=114.1 mph on our reference T driver and with HCP=0.
golfer A a representative golfer with CHD=251 yards and HS=100.7 mph on our reference T driver and with HCP=10.
golfer B a representative golfer with CHD=217 yards and H=87.2 mph on our reference T driver and with HCP=20.

golfer C a representative golfer with CHD=179 yards and HS=73.8 mph on our reference T driver and with HCP=27.5.
HCP handicap.
HS [mph] head speed, speed of the cg of the head just prior to impact.
LA [deg] loft angle.*
POF hits partly off the face hits for those hits near the edge of the face for which more than 25% of the imprint area would be off the face.
* More detail will be found for these items in the Appendix.

club face. Both things affect the percent of hits that are POF.

HS values for the table were arbitrarily set at 114.1, 100.7, 87.2, and 73.8 mph as HCP increased from 0 to 30, approximating golfers P, A, B, and C (modified to HCP 30) respectively.

The table shows that driver B has slightly more POF hits than driver A, even though driver A has less face area. This is because the face of driver A is rather high at the toe and is thus a better match to the hit pattern.

The table shows that driver D provides a remarkable improvement over the others, because it has a large elliptical shape and its toe is tilted prominently upward, so both outline shape and tilt approximately match the hit pattern.

Figures 17-2, 17-3, 17-4, and 17-5 illustrate POF hits on representative driver faces for golfer C with HCP = 30. As noted in the figure captions, drivers A and B are the same as in Table 17-1. Comparison of Figures 17-3 and 17-4 confirms that face shape is much improved when its long axis is tilted up at the toe end, so that at impact, it is a better match to the upward tilt of the hit pattern.

Large area is desirable and Figure 17-5 represents a rather extreme size which is much larger than other driver faces. Its face is somewhat larger than driver D of Table 17-1 and is near to the upper limits of face strength and of tolerable air drag which was discussed in Chapter 16.

For best results with a large face club such as driver D, the ball should be teed up a little higher than usual. Otherwise hits cannot be made on the upper part of the face and some of its advantage is lost. Standard 2-1/8 inch tees may be used with minimal insertion depth into the turf. The longer 2-3/8 inch size is better.

Most of these features do not apply to fairway woods and irons because of the absence of a tee. Our research suggests that they should have faces which are long in the toe-heel direction. Modern designs of irons and fairway woods have a definite trend in this direction.

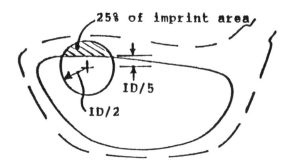

Fig. 17-1 *Our definition of a POF hit. It means that more than 25% of the normal imprint area is off the face. Note that the ball diameter is much larger than the imprint diameter in these figures.*

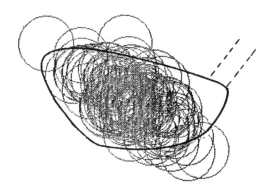

Fig. 17-2 *The scatter of imprints on driver A of Table 17-1. 13.0% of hits are POF hits. Golfer C*

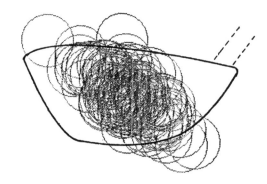

Fig. 17-3 *The scatter of imprints with driver B of Table 17-1. 14.1% of hits are POF hits. Golfer C*

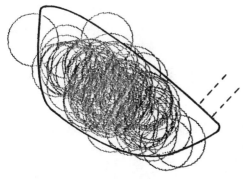

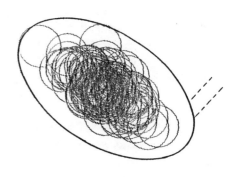

Fig. 17-4 *The scatter of imprints with driver B of Table 17-1 which is also tilted upward at the toe. 2.8% POF. Golfer C. (Not shown in Table 17-1.)*

Fig. 17-5 *The scatter of imprints with experimental 8.1 sq in elliptical face and tilted upward at the toe. 0.2% POF. Golfer C. (Not shown in Table 17-1.)*

Table 17-1 *The effects of AOF and face outline of several driver types on the percentage of POF hits. AOF means the minimum percentage of imprint area off the face which counts as a POF hit. Driver A is a laminated wooden driver, representative of designs of about 1985. Driver B is a large head driver introduced in about 1995. Driver C is a somewhat larger driver which has been popular in Japan. Driver D is our preliminary driver design with large elliptical face, tilted up at the toe. Areas are in square inches.*

AOF, %	HCP	percent POF			
		driver A area 3.79	driver B area 4.30	driver C area 4.75	driver D area 6.05
3	0	9.8	10.8	6.5	0.0
10	0	4.2	4.7	2.4	0.0
25	0	0.6	0.8	0.3	0.0
50	0	0.0	0.0	0.0	0.0
3	10	18.9	20.0	13.0	0.7
10	10	13.8	14.2	9.6	0.3
25	10	7.8	8.3	4.2	0.0
50	10	0.8	1.2	0.5	0.0
3	20	27.6	29.0	23.6	2.8
10	20	21.0	22.2	17.8	1.2
25	20	10.2	11.4	9.0	0.2
50	20	4.1	3.5	2.4	0.0
3	30	31.5	33.2	25.1	6.1
10	30	24.0	25.7	19.9	3.2
25	30	13.9	15.0	10.4	0.9
50	30	7.0	8.1	4.8	0.2

TECHNICAL NOTES

To study POF hits, we programmed a computer to generate the typical distribution of a golfer's hit pattern for each handicap we wanted to consider. We used a system of 343 statistically weighted hits for each face (Hermite-Gauss Quadrature, order 7 for 3 golfer errors).

The computer then found the percentage of POF hits, using AOF = 25% as discussed below. Equations (1) and (2) in Chapter 4 show how we varied the size of the elliptical distributions for that calculation.

It was necessary to specify the percent of area of the ball imprint which was off the face before it was counted as a POF hit. We found a reasonable way to make this decision. We know the peak load distribution at impact with reasonable accuracy from a detailed study of static loads on balls. Our results are similar to others which have been reported.

The load per unit area (that is, pressure) varies radially over the area of the imprint. Pressure is greatest at the center and diminishes rapidly so that near the edge of the imprint, pressure is nearly negligible for our case.

This means that when a small part of the outer edge of the imprint is off the face, it makes only a small change in the magnitude and direction of force on the ball and thus the launch direction is not much changed. In addition, the deformation of the ball is changed only a little, which means the amount of the impact force and the coefficients of restitution are not much changed. Thus, the direction and distance are not greatly affected when only a small part of the impact is off the face.

We believe that when only 10 or 15% of the area is off the face the effect is small and that when more than about 40 or 50% is off, the effect is large. After considering these things and Table 17-1, we concluded that it was reasonable to consider a hit to be POF only when 25% or more of the imprint area is off the face.

Figure 17-1 shows to scale, an imprint area which is 25% off the face. In considering Figures 17-1 through 17-5, remember that the actual ball diameter is much larger than the imprint diameters shown.

For all of the figures and calculations, the distortion of imprint shape caused by POF hits was disregarded. It would be a significant complication to allow for this distortion of the imprint shape and we believe that disregarding it has not significantly altered the conclusions discussed.

This makes it practical to calculate reasonably accurate comparisons of the percent POF hits for various drivers, given the description of the face outline.

OPTIMUM FACE CURVATURE FOR GOLF CLUBS

Y OU PROBABLY KNOW THAT THE FACE OF YOUR DRIVER HAS BULGE AND ROLL CURVATURE. IF IT IS NOT JUST RIGHT YOUR TEE SHOTS HAVE MUCH MORE SCATTER. HERE'S A NEW FACE SURFACE SHAPE WHICH IS GREATLY IMPROVED. THE RESULT IS MORE SHOTS IN THE FAIRWAY.

SIDE SPIN

An ideal center hit gives the ball pure "backspin" which means it is spinning about a strictly horizontal axis. When the clubhead is not square to its direction of travel at impact, there is a component of rotation around a vertical axis which means the spin axis of golf ball is no longer horizontal. "Side spin" or "non-horizontal orientation of the spin axis" are equivalent ways to express the effect.

Other than the clubhead not being square to its direction of travel, off-center hits toward the toe or heel of woods are another important cause of side spin. In this case, proper face curvature and large clubhead inertia can reduce the errors caused by these off-center hits.

SLICES AND HOOKS

Side spin causes changes in the side curvature, direction, height, and distance of the shot and corresponding changes in the stop point of the shot.

The side spin due to off-center hits is caused by rotation of the clubhead while in contact with the ball during impact. It has been long recognized and has often been called the gear effect. The head rotation which causes the gear effect is widely thought of as being rotation around the cg of the head as a result of

off-center impact. This is incorrect and often by a large margin.

The rotation is around the center of percussion which may be located many inches away from the cg for hits which are only a small distance toward toe or heel from the cg or only a fraction of an inch away for hits far toward the toe or heel. Center of percussion is well known in the realm of physical mechanics.

Side spin (regardless of its cause) governs side curvature (hook or slice) of the shot and thus, how far a shot will be off line.

REDUCING SIDE SPIN (GETTING STRAIGHT SHOTS)

Clubhead rotation causing side spin due to off-center hits is reduced when the moment of inertia about the vertical axis is large. The other 5 moment of inertia terms are less important. Compact heads necessarily have low moment of inertia, and therefore are much more prone to slices and hooks than large heads. Optimum face surface curvature can substantially reduce lateral scatter of stop points caused by toe-heel off-center hits.

For center hits, straight shots and maximum distance are the design goal. The principal clubhead design features to achieve this goal are the optimum combination of cg location, LA, HW and CLG.

To minimize scatter from off-center hits, face surface shape and large moments of inertia (mainly around the vertical and toe-heel axes) are the main design variables. Optimizing these factors is an important design goal.

Heretofore, all driver designs reduced errors due to off-center hits by curving the club face surface as defined by a chosen bulge radius (a curvature in the toe-heel direction.) Designers have gained much experience by careful study of the effects of bulge. It is remarkable how well they have done, considering

SYMBOLS AND DEFINITIONS		
BR [in] bulge radius.*	**HS**	[mph] head speed, speed of the cg
cg [ ] center of gravity (more accurately, center of mass); its location is usually given in inches.		of the head just prior to impact.
	HW	[gm] head weight (mass), weight of the head without shaft.
CLG [in] club length.*	**LA**	[deg] loft angle.*
fairway frame the coordinate system having its origin at the center of the ball at impact, with X axis toward the heel of the club, Y axis vertical upwards and Y axis toward the target.*	**POF hits**	partly off the face hits for those hits near the edge of the face for which more that 25% of the imprint area would be off the face.
	RR	roll radius.*
		More detail will be found for these items in the Appendix.
HCP handicap.		

the complexity of the problem.

The experimental difficulty is that the optimum face surface shape depends on HW, HS, LA, cg location, 6 moment of inertia terms, and several other variables. It is nearly impossible to experimentally evaluate effects on the optimum bulge radius of each of these variables individually and for all in combination.

Similar curvature corrections have been used for up-down errors, but for reasons which have usually not been well understood. This up-down curvature is called the roll radius.

At first, we used our model to calculate the optimum bulge and roll radii to yield a minimum scatter of stop points as measured by the average of the radial errors of the stop points from the stop point of the center hit. These optimized results were better than the bulge and roll values used on most woods because they cope appropriately with all of the variables listed above, without the complications of the experimental methods.

New Concept in Surface Curvature
Then we began to consider if some other kind of curved shape might be a further improvement. This investigation opened the door to distinctly superior shapes, compared to the simple bulge and roll surfaces.

We found that for optimum design, the surface typically curves mainly from the face center toward the toe and upward, and toward the heel and upward. Curvature is very different going from the face center in the opposite directions. For most driver designs, the result gives a flat or only slightly curved area below the face center.

Face Curvature Examples
Figure 18-1 shows contour lines of various driver faces. The contour lines are similar to topographic maps of terrain in that they show various levels of the surface.

The optimum face surface shape with our large face driver design is shown in A in the figure. For comparison, the other 3 surface shapes shown are representative of typical driver designs currently on the market. On an actual club, these variations are often not very apparent.

Our special surface shape is easier to compare with another if you look nearly parallel to each

face at a grazing angle. It helps when the faces are clean and shiny so that you can see reflections in the surface.

Another way to see the difference is to hold the edge of a ruler against each of the faces in various locations.

Table 18-1 shows the reduced scatter of stop points caused by this improved face surface design, without considering POF hits (they are considered in Chapter 17). Drivers A, B, and C are compared.

Driver A is one of our large-face driver designs with its optimized face surface shape. Driver B is a popular modern large head driver, and Driver C is a traditional wood driver popular from about 1960 to 1985.

The scatter of stop points has been calculated as if each driver had the optimized face surface shape (the lines in the table with bold letters); as if it had a flat face with no bulge or roll; and with the bulge and roll radius (BR and RR) as manufactured, except for club A which was manufactured with the optimized surface rather than bulge and roll.

Results for longer hits are similar, but errors are larger and the improvement for the optimized face surface shape is greater. For golfers with rather low handicap (HCP), ideal face curvature is rather important, but less so than for less-skilled golfers with a high HCP. We found that the optimum face curvature depended only slightly on HCP.

Table 18-1 shows that even for a flat face, driver A had much smaller scatter than with the flat faces on B or C. This is mainly because Driver A has much larger inertia terms and its cg location is closer to optimum. Driver C has low inertia terms, its cg is much too high, and its RR and BR values were not well-chosen (even worse than a flat face.)

Optimizing the face shapes made good improvements for drivers B and C as compared with the manufactured bulge and roll and even more, compared with the flat face.

It is particularly important for good design that driver A has average errors which are 5 to 15 yards less than the others. Golfers have found this improvement to be readily perceptible.

Similar improvements are possible for fairway woods, but for irons with the cg much farther forward, improvements are less and different in nature, and are essentially negligible for putters.

Patents are pending on our new surface shapes.

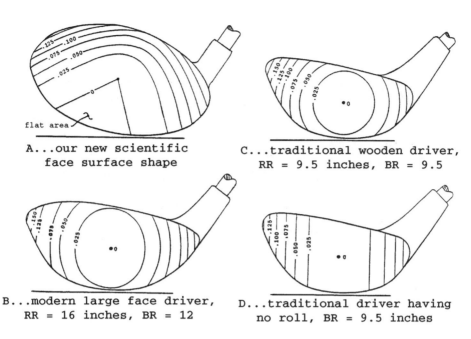

A...our new scientific
face surface shape

C...traditional wooden driver,
RR = 9.5 inches, BR = 9.5

B...modern large face driver,
RR = 16 inches, BR = 12

D...traditional driver having
no roll, BR = 9.5 inches

Fig. 18-1 *Contour lines which reveal the face surface shape for 4 drivers. The numbers on the curves are the distances in inches of the curved surface aft of a plane tangent to the face at the face center. The flat area for driver A is indicated. It is absent for other drivers.*

Table 18-1 *Errors of stop points for drivers without considering POF hits for 3 face shapes: optimized face shapes (opt), conventional bulge/roll faces (B-R), and flat faces. ME is the average radial error in yards for a 25 handicap golfer with 205 yard drives. BR and RR are bulge radius and roll radius in inches. Ra and Rb are governing radii for optimized face surfaces. Clubs A, B, and C are defined in Figure 18-1. The mark "--" indicates that entries are not applicable.*

club	face type	optimized face Ra	optimized face Rb	bulge/roll face RR	bulge/roll face BR	ME yards	change in ME yards
A	opt	7.4	10.5	--	--	25.80	0
A	flat	--	--	--	--	30.97	5.17
A	B-R	--	--	--		--	--
B	opt	6.9	9.5	--	--	28.35	2.55
B	flat	--	--	--	--	35.32	9.52
B	B-R	--	--	12	16	30.28	4.48
C	opt	9.2	10.1	--	--	35.65	9.85
C	flat	--	--	--	--	37.88	12.08
C	B-R	--	--	9.5	9.5	42.42	16.62

TECHNICAL NOTES

Our procedure was to operate the model with the normally distributed hit pattern, and optimize results by having the computer model systematically adjust curvature variables and orientations by the Simplex method for minimum scatter of stop points.

We found that circular, elliptical, parabolic, exponential, and similar face surface shapes are almost equally satisfactory. This is mainly because only a small portion of such curves is useful over the span of the face and all closely approximate a circular shape. In addition, the distribution of hits is concentrated near the center of the face, so the sparsely scattered hits near the periphery are much less important, being less numerous. For convenience, we used an elliptical shape.

BEHAVIOR OF GOLF CLUB SHAFTS

A "BETTER MOUSETRAP" MAY NOT BE YOUR DELIVERANCE IN SELECTING CLUBS. HERE, YOU'LL FIND OUT THAT THE BEST SHAFT FOR A DRIVER IS A LITTLE DIFFERENT FROM THE USUAL CONCEPT.

INTRODUCTION TO SHAFT BENDING

The club shaft bends backward at the beginning of a golfer's down swing. It is conventionally believed that the shaft then vibrates forward at about the same time as the clubhead hits the ball, in what is sometimes referred to as a "whip" effect.

This forward vibration is then believed to increase HS at impact and improve distance, especially for golfers who have a slow swing such as ladies and seniors. While this sounds plausible, actually this concept of the shaft whipping forward is a minor effect and has little to do with HS at impact as we will explain.

Our experiments confirm the shaft does bend during the swing in a somewhat different way and for a different reason. You can easily try some of these experiments yourself.

We started this examination of shafts in about 1990, and since then, References 5, 6, and 11 have appeared, which reach many of the same conclusions regarding the negligible effect of forward whipping of the shaft. Milne and Davis (Reference 11) give a particularly convincing discussion which is in condensed form in Reference 4. Various other papers in References 4, 5, and 6 describe detailed studies of shaft dynamics, but most do not appear to allow for the flexible wrist joint. This is a fundamental omission, as you will see.

High speed photos (using excellent equipment) of drivers and other woods show that the shaft is bent backward at the beginning of the swing and forward at the time of impact. Thus photos tend to show what the whipping concept seems to explain, and you may wonder why we disagree.

The forward bend is observed for woods but it is much smaller or absent with irons. That is sometimes explained away because irons have stiffer shafts.

Consider Figure 19-1. You might want to get help from a friend and try this experiment with a driver. Hold the grip down firmly against the table and have your friend pull the clubhead upward a few inches then quickly let go. The club will vibrate violently, oscillating back and forth. You might conclude that this confirms the current ideas, but there are other important experiments.

Look carefully at Figure 19-2. This is the real situation when a golfer swings a club. There is no rigid table top. There is only the golfer holding the club. Again, hold the grip firmly and have your friend pull the clubhead to one side and quickly let go. Now, no matter how firmly you try to hold the club, it won't vibrate violently as shown in the experiment illustrated in Figure 19-1. The vibrations die out almost immediately.

In thinking about this vibration, think in terms of the vibration motion being added to the basic swinging motion of a non-bending club shaft and head. It is this added vibration motion with which we are concerned.

Several reasons explain why vibration or whipping forward is erroneous. One is that a golfer's hands can't hold the grip nearly as rigidly as the table or a vise. The hands and wrists do not weigh enough

SYMBOLS AND DEFINITIONS			
cg	[] center of gravity (more accurately, center of mass); its location is usually given in inches.		different from LA because centrifugal force bends the shaft and at impact, somewhat changes clubhead orientation.*
dHS	[%] standard deviation of HS just prior to impact as a percent of HS.	FA	[deg] face angle.*
HCP	handicap.	FAE	[deg] effective FA, somewhat different from FA because centrifugal force bends the shaft and at impact, somewhat changes clubhead orientation.
HS	[mph] head speed, speed of the cg of the head just prior to impact.		
HW	[gm] head weight (mass), weight of the head without shaft.		
LA	[deg] loft angle.*		* More detail will be found for these items in the Appendix.
LAE	[deg] effective LA, somewhat		

and are far less rigid than a sturdy table top. Furthermore, the vibration dies out quickly. It may not even complete the first half cycle of vibration from one side to the other. Hands cushion the movement and quickly remove the vibration energy. An engineer refers to this in terms such as vibration damping, end conditions, or mechanical impedance.

We have made strobe photos of vibrations of a driver when it is held in a golfer's hands as shown in Figure 19-3. We used a conventional size metal wood with a steel shaft. Other shafts and heads give similar results.

Prior to the vibration, we kept the shaft bent with a strong string tied from the grip to the tip of a small, lightweight bar attached under the clubhead and extending out about 4 inches beyond the toe, as shown in Figure 19-3. We put small patches of reflecting tape on the shaft and the clubhead and used strobe lighting. Then we cut the string and took short time exposure pictures showing dots of light from the stroboscope. This test showed the kind of motion described above for Figure 19-2. The vibration died out almost before the shaft had moved back to its rest position.

If the photos of golfers swinging woods show the shaft bending forward, how can that happen if the vibration dies out? The answer is that something else causes the forward bending. That something else is centripetal force (more commonly called centrifugal force).

THE REAL CAUSE OF SHAFT BENDING

Centrifugal force appears when the clubhead travels in a curved path. The golfer holds onto the club's grip keeping the clubhead in a circular path and experiences the pull of the centrifugal force. This is well known in physics and engineering and can be easily calculated with high accuracy.

We studied a number of photos of golfers and made strobe photos of the swing. From these photos, we found the curvature of the path and this allowed us to calculate centrifugal force. We found that the golfer must pull on the club grip of a driver in response to the centrifugal force with a force well over 100 pounds for a very fast swing and about 30 or 40 pounds for a slow swing.

This is probably the main reason why golfers get blisters and calluses on their hands. It is surprising that the force is so large. It doesn't pull the golfer and cause him to fall forward only because it lasts for such a short time.

For a driver, the cg of the head is located an inch or more toward the toe from the shaft axis and an inch or more rearward. For an iron, it is toward the toe but only slightly rearward. Centrifugal force is directed away from the grip end of the shaft and acts at the cg of the head. This force is somewhat off the shaft center line, which is why it bends the shaft. This bending changes the orientation of the head at impact.

Consider an experiment with extremely flexible shafts such as illustrated in Figure 19-4. The small circles in the clubhead represent the cg location. Suppose your shaft had a very flexible section like a hinged joint so it could easily bend as in case A of the figure. If this joint is down near the clubhead, the head would swing to an extreme angle of about 90 degrees. If the joint is anywhere near the central half of the shaft length, good hits are possible with some practice. If it is near the grip, the club would be nearly impossible to use during the backswing but the angular position of the head is not much affected by bending at this joint. Centrifugal force explains these changes of orientation of the head but the vibration ideas do not.

HOW SHAFT BENDING
ALTERS EFFECTIVE LA AND FA

Figure 19-4 also vividly illustrates one reason why LAE and FAE differ from LA and FA, depending strongly on shaft stiffness and how the stiffness is distributed.

A training club is advertised which has a hinge partway up the shaft such as at case C in the figure. With practice, a golfer can make good hits, closely approximating good hits with a normal shaft, whether his HS is low or high. It helps to illustrate the way centrifugal force bends the shaft.

Figure 19-4 illustrates various other cases for a hinged shaft. It shows that centrifugal force tends to move the cg of the head so as to bring it in line with the grip end of the shaft axis.

For best performance, the clubhead should be designed to reasonably suit the shaft to be used with it. This is because the shaft bending somewhat opens FA and increases LA. For example, the head for the extreme case A could be designed so that it had the appropriate LAE and FAE. This would be a very strange looking head, but it illustrates the point. In more realistic cases such as B and C, much smaller revisions would be needed for LA and FA.

For real shafts, such head design adjustments to suit LAE and FAE are small, but too large to disregard. This is particularly true for high HS, but it is not negligible even for low HS.

There is an additional effect. Shaft bending varies with a golfer's unintended HS variations (dHS) with corresponding variations of LAE and FAE, which in turn, cause variations of the stop point. The changes of LAE and FAE are greater with higher HS and more flexible shafts. Thus, it is more important for shaft stiffness in about the lower 30% to be high for high HS. Although less important for low HS, nothing is gained for low HS by use of a flexible shaft.

Shaft stiffness is important in club design.

STIFFNESS MEASUREMENT
It would be valuable for golf if all shaft manufacturers stated stiffness in a universal, suitable way. Our method of measurement is illustrated in Figures 19-5 and 19-6. See Technical Notes for the calculations. Our method avoids the erroneous vise-like clamping of the grip which was discussed at the beginning of this chapter.

This sub-model again leads to the important conclusion that although stiff shafts are important for golfers of high HS and less important for golfers with low HS, there is no advantage for flexible shafts for golfers of low HS.

In Reference 4, Milne suggests a good way for golfers to quickly estimate shaft stiffness: hold the grip and press the toe end downward into the turf. Stiff shafts bend less than flexible shafts. Remember that with a large head, the toe end is farther from the shaft axis and also increases the bend, so the test is best done with heads which are similar.

FEEL
The shaft has a strong effect on feel. We distinguish 2 kinds of feel: the feel during the back swing and down swing (the "swing feel"); and the feel resulting from impact (the "impact feel"). We have done little research on this subject.

We have often heard from golfers that no feel is the best feel, which seems reasonable. Nevertheless,

we believe that after becoming accustomed to it, golfers would learn to like nearly any kind of feel if the club performs perceptibly better. That is, we believe they would learn to associate any particular feel with good performance and consider it to be a good feel.

In particular, golfers experience impact feel after the impact and the ball is well on its way. It takes a little time for the vibrations to be transmitted up the shaft and the ball is some distance from the clubhead when the vibration reaches the grip.

We have disregarded impact feel in considering optimum designs. It is our experience that there is minimal impact feel for clubheads designed for optimum LA and cg location as determined by the model.

THE SPINE EFFECT (LATERAL BENDING)
Recently, the "spine" in club shafts has become an increasingly popular subject in articles and in advertising. The spine idea apparently started with the observation that the near-undetectable weld seam up the side of a steel shaft may cause it to bend easier in one direction than in another. Further study showed that slight nonuniformities cause unequal bending for all typical shafts, regardless of the material.

We measured bending characteristics of several graphite and steel shafts. Study of the structural loading on the shaft during a swing shows that the central part of the shaft may bow out toward toe or heel, but only very slightly, and that centrifugal force on the clubhead nearly eliminates corresponding movement of the clubhead itself. Lateral movement of the clubhead is only a fraction of the thickness of a paper match.

We analyzed the effects where the ball stops on the fairway for drivers with various combinations of the spine effect. We found that under the worst conditions, the spine effect we measured would move the stop points only a negligible amount, and would not increase their scatter appreciably. Testing with more shafts is unlikely to change this conclusion

FIRMNESS OF GRIP
The section above, "The Real Cause of Shaft Bending", shows that centrifugal force may be 30 or 40 pounds for a slow swing and 100 or more for a strong swing. These forces are not estimates; they are

soundly based on simple theory. It mentions that these large forces do not make a golfer fall forward only because the forces last a very short time. The forces are probably the main cause of calluses.

This makes us very skeptical of the common advice to take a light grip, and sometimes even, never vary the grip pressure during the swing. It seems necessary for golfers to use a rather firm grip, conven-

tional advice notwithstanding.

If you doubt the need to use a firm, even strong grip, make a simple experiment. Stand on a bench or chair with a club, to which you have tied a 50 to 100 pound dumb bell or other weight and see how hard you must grip. A short iron or putter may make this more convenient.

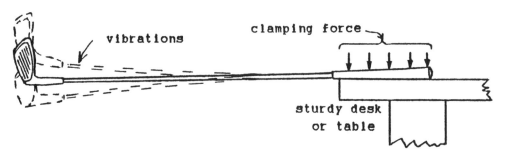

Fig. 19-1 *Vibrations of a golf club when its grip is held firmly against a rigid table or desk. To demonstrate this, hold the grip firmly against the table then ask a friend to pull up on the clubhead and quickly let go. It oscillates vigorously up and down.*

Fig. 19-2 *Vibrations of a golf club when its grip is held by a golfer in the usual way. To demonstrate this, ask a friend to pull up on the clubhead and quickly let go, as for Fig. 19-1. You will need to hold the grip quite firmly. The vibration is very different from Fig. 19-1.*

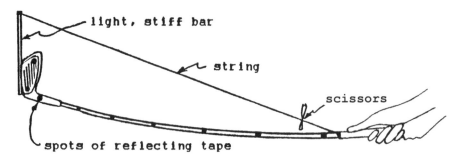

Fig. 19-3 *Our setup for making strobe photos of the vibration. Vibrations start when the string is cut.*

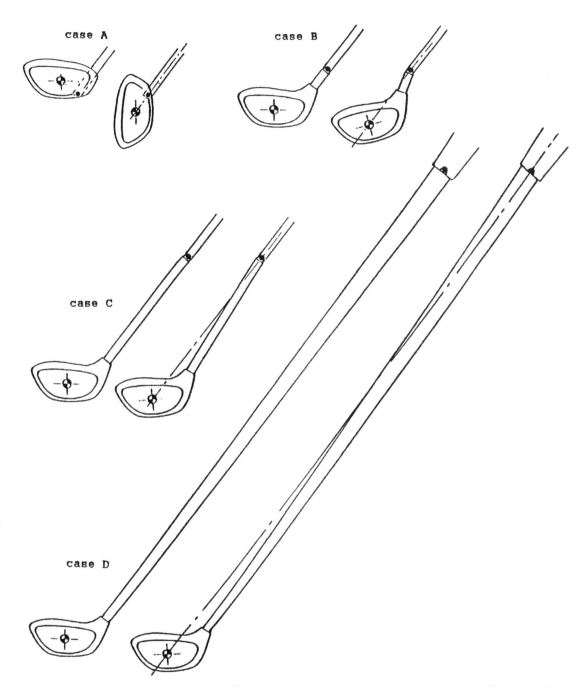

Fig. 19-4 *Examples of cases which show the effects at the time of impact for extremely low bending stiffness, the effects of where it is located, and the importance of designing the head to match the shaft stiffness characteristics. Case A is an imaginary extreme where bending happens at a very low position, case B is for a rather low location, case C is for a rather high location, and case D is for an extremely high location. In each case, a shaft is shown with very high stiffness for comparison.* **High stiffness in about the lower 30% of the shaft is particularly important.**

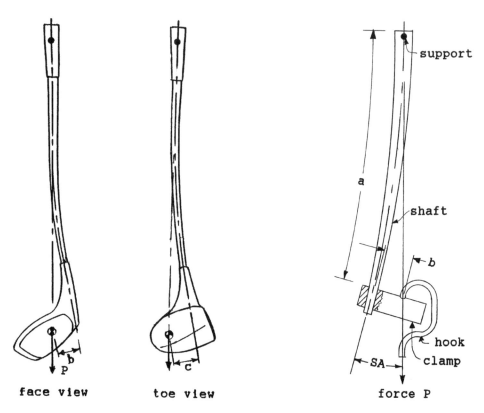

Fig. 19-5 *The effect of centrifugal force on the orientation of a driver head at the time of impact. The toe view shows that the force P with moment arm C increases LA. The face view shows a similar effect in which the toe deflects down, mainly increasing the face angle with a small effect on LA.*

Fig. 19-6 *A method of measuring shaft stiffness in the laboratory. It simulates the effect of centrifugal force on the head and shows how the shaft bends.*

TECHNICAL NOTES

Shaft stiffness

Shaft bending can be closely modeled by a beam hinged at the top end with an eccentric tensile load at the free end which represents the centrifugal force at the cg of the head. The shaft itself has relatively little mass and still less centrifugal force effects so its mass may reasonably be neglected for purposes of studying centrifugal bending. Being hinged at the top end, this test approximates a golfer whose wrists are much less stiff in bending than a shaft, a reasonable approximation.

If the shaft were perfectly rigid, the "shaft angle" (SA) in Figure 19-6 would then have the value "rigid shaft angle" (RSA) which is arctan(b/a). This is as if the load P were very small, and all parts were weightless.

We are concerned with the deflection angle of the head (DA) when the load P is applied, since this represents the change in orientation of the head when the load P is the actual centrifugal force at the time of impact.

When the load is applied, the observed shaft angle is SA and thus SA = RSA + DA.

Theory for a uniform beam (which is a good approximation) with these end conditions with combined axial load and bending moment allows DA to be calculated:

(1)   DA = SA − RSA [deg], where

(2)   DA = (b/a) ∗ (n ∗ a/tanh(n ∗ a) − 1) ∗ 180/π [deg],

(3)   RSA = arctan(b/a) [deg}, and

(4)   EI = P/n^2 [lbf/in^2], where EI means shaft stiffness, n is calculated from equation (2), and a [in], b [in], and P [lbf] are defined lin Figure 19-6.

The shaft stiffness measurement thus uses the following steps.

• First, measure b and a then calculate RSA from equation (3).
• Second, measure SA with load P applied. P should approximate the centrifugal force in a swing, such as 50 to 100 lbf and b should be approximately the distance from the shaft axis to the cg. This provides the value of DA from equation (1).
• Third, use this value in equation (2), and solve for the remaining unknown, n, by iteration.
• Finally find EI from equation (4).

We use the result in our impact model. The same equations are programmed to find DA with known values for EI, P, a, and b.

It is important that such measurements represent changes from the unloaded positions to avoid confusion of results due to shafts which are not perfectly straight. More on this below.

EI, found in this way, is the effective shaft stiffness parameter. It is independent of P and b, but it is necessary to avoid small P and small b because small values degrade accuracy of the EI calculation.

A simplified alternate may deserve further study for finding EI. This is to clamp the tip of the shaft in a rigid mounting, then apply a transverse load near the butt end and measure the deflection where the load is applied. This treats the shaft as a cantilever beam. The deflection is primarily governed by the bending stiffness near the tip, with negligible dependence of bending stiffness toward the butt end, and this approximation also applies to Figure 19-6. This bends the tip in nearly the same way as in Figure 19-6.

With this approximation, the shaft may be considered as a uniform beam for which EI = F ∗ L^3/3 ∗ x, where F is the transverse force, L is the distance from the clamp to where F is applied, and x is the lateral deflection at that point.

When EI is evaluated in this way, n can be found from equation (4) as SQR(P/EI) and substituted into equation (2) to find DA.

We have made a few tests of this cantilever beam method and it appears to give results within a few percentage points of the direct test method. More comparison testing should be done to see if the cantilever method is sufficiently accurate for the purpose, because it is considerably simpler. Such tests could also compare EI as measured by these methods, for a strictly uniform tube to an actual tapered shaft, to evaluate the uniform beam approximation.

We suggest that manufacturers provide shaft stiffness data on their various shaft designs by measurement of the effective value of EI.

Grip effects

In our first test, we consider the golfer's wrists to be a free hinge at the time of impact. More research would be desirable to measure the representative mechanical impedance of a golfer's grip, although grip impedance is a small factor.

The mechanical impedance of the grip could be approximated by static measurements. A golfer could use a firm grip on a club having a long rope tied to the head and pull with 50 to 100 pounds force. He would then make a strong effort to bend the shaft upward and downward with his wrists. The resulting angle is measured. Real effects might be estimated at 5 to 20% of this.

If this has negligible effect on the angle DA, a free hinge approximation is valid, as we expect. If this effect is significant, a more elaborate end condition would need to be used in place of the free hinge.

Unsymmetric shaft bending ("spine")

To understand the spine effect, we must recognize that shafts are not perfect and are typically slightly stiffer when bent in one direction and less stiff in another. If the butt is rigidly clamped and a load is applied at the tip to bend the shaft, it will bend in the normal way as expected when bent in its most or least stiff orientation. If bent at intermediate orientations, it bends slightly sidewise in addition to the bend in the expected direction. It is supposed that any sidewise bending toward toe or heel will cause off-center hits.

The spine effect is thought to cause one club to behave differently from another. When the effect is considered for one club alone, it is thought to change the hit pattern toward the toe or heel.

We studied the problem to find out whether or not the effects of such bending are sufficient to cause significant errors in the stop points of shots with drivers, both for the case of variations of a particular club and for variations from one club to another in a set.

The shaft bends back somewhat, early in the down swing. We studied the lateral bending during this phase and concluded that it does not move the clubhead significantly out of the swing plane.

A golfer's wrists are like a hinge rather than a clamped end. Centrifugal force pulls outward on the clubhead, strongly resisting any tendency for the head to move laterally.

Thus if the shaft bends laterally due to the spine effect, the wrists bend slightly and the clubhead is not moved significantly aside. The lateral bend of the shaft is a slightly bowed shape.

Another factor is that the amount of lateral bending is very small even when measured with the butt rigidly clamped.

We measured bending stiffness for 4 driver shafts, 1 of steel and the other 3 graphite of low and high quality as judged by their cost. We found that the lateral bending for typical downswings is no more than about .03 or .04 inch.

This small amount of bending should be considered in the light of centrifugal force strongly tending to reduce it. We conclude that the spine effect causes negligible movement of the head toward toe or heel.

However, there is another effect which depends on the spine idea. The centrifugal force bends the shaft near the tip as described in connection with Figure 19-4. At the bottom of the swing, this bend changes the effective loft and face angles of the clubhead and the center of gravity (cg) of the head moves slightly downward.

We measured tip bending stiffness of the 4 shafts and found that typically, the maximum stiffness was less than 6% above the minimum stiffness. We also found that the maximum downward movement of the cg was about .04 inch greater than the minimum movement. The worst shaft had changes only a little greater than these.

We changed inputs for our computer model to correspond to these changes in stiffness and movement of the head. This indicates the changes in stop point of the ball after hits if nothing changed except that the shaft was changed from its mean orientation to its stiffest or to its least stiff orientation.

For the most detrimental combination of these changes, we found that CHD changed no more than .33 yard from the CHD for the mean stiffness and for the cg in its mean position.

Similarly, we found that the lateral position for center hits moved no more than .57 yard; and average scatter of the hits changed no more than .12 yard. Of course, in actual golf, the shaft orientation doesn't change, so these numbers represent variations far greater than a golfer would experience.

In our study of spines, we also measured the straightness of the shafts. Although shafts are nearly straight, they caused misalignments of the measured shaft axis which were not negligible compared to the variations of bending being measured.

It is essential to avoid, or to correct for, shaft straightness in measuring the spine effect. It was not always clear that this was done in descriptions of spine measurements which we have seen. We found the axis of the tip to be misaligned as much as .3 degree from the axis through the butt.

Bending of a uniform beam with differing bending stiffnesses (the "spine" problem) is discussed in textbooks such as Reference 10. Lateral bending effects are easily calculated. Club shafts are not uniform, but the important bending is near the tip and this part of a shaft has reasonably uniform stiffness.

Recently we learned of a report stating that changing the orientation of the spine has a reasonably large effect on the scatter of hits on the club face. Golfers made numerous hits and hit patterns on the club face were measured for each. Then the test was interrupted and unknown to the golfers, the clubs were reshafted with shafts having proper spine orientation.

The same test was repeated and it was found that scatter of hits on the face was much reduced. The golfers apparently were aware that something had changed between their test hits.

A suggestion for better tests is to provide a golfer with 2 identical clubs which have identical shafts exhibiting a reasonably large spine effect. One would be oriented in an optimum way and one in a poor way. Golfers would then try each one without knowing their identities. The first few trial shots with each club would be ignored. Rather than hit patterns on the face, measured stop points would be studied to indicate the effect. This might be repeated with a second pair having markedly different LA.

Our evidence indicates that spine effects cause insignificant errors.

SELECTION OF A CLUB SHAFT AND GRIP

HOW IMPORTANT IS SHAFT WEIGHT, GRIP WEIGHT, SHAFT LENGTH AND STIFFNESS? THIS CHAPTER GIVES ANSWERS AND SOME SURPRISES; FOR EXAMPLE, STEEL SHAFTS ARE JUST FINE FOR IRONS.

In the previous chapter, we showed that shaft bending is primarily due to centrifugal force and that the idea of forward whipping effects is essentially erroneous. When the shaft bends, the head has a new orientation, there is a corresponding small increase in LAE, and FAE becomes more open (FAE decreases). The amount of change depends on HS.

SYMBOLS AND DEFINITIONS	
CA [deg] contact angle which is the acute angle between the direction of travel of the club head cg and a level plane at the time of impact.*	different from LA because the shaft bends and the head may be rotated at impact.*
CHD [yd] center hit distance.*	**MD** [yd] maximum distance, the value of CHD with a specific shaft and grip and with specific values of HW, CLG, and HS with no golfer errors and when the head design is optimized for this condition.
cg center of gravity.*	
CLG [in] club length (more accurately, measured from the top of the grip to the intersection of the shaft axis with the X-Z plane when the club is held at the address position.)	
FA [deg] face angle.*	**reference D driver** imaginary ultimate driver design having 40 gram shaft, CLG = 48 inches, 180 gram head, and 20 gram grip, design optimized for each HS in question.
FAE [deg] effective FA, somewhat different from FA because the shaft bends and the head may be rotated at impact.*	**reference T driver** a driver with 88 gram graphite shaft, CLG = 43 inches, HW = 200 grams, and 43.5 gram grip which we used in golfer tests and for frequent reference. Notice that modern drivers usually give up 4 to 5 yards greater CHD than this reference.
golfer P a representative golfer with CHD = 281 yards and HS = 114.1 mph on our Reference T driver and with HCP = 0.	
golfer A a representative golfer with CHD = 251 yards and H = 100.7 mph on our Reference T driver and with HCP = 10.	
golfer B a representative golfer with CHD = 217 yards and HS = 87.2 mph on our Reference T driver and with HCP = 20.	**SPA** [deg] swing plane angle between the normal to the swing plane and the Y axis.*
golfer C a representative golfer with CHD = 179 yards and HS = 73.8 mph on our Reference T driver and with HCP = 27.5.	**UMD** [yd] ultimate maximum CHD with reference D driver for any particular golfer class.
HS [mph] head speed, speed of the cg of the head just prior to impact.	**Xcg** [in] X location of the cg in the head frame, see Fig 2-1.
	Ycg [in] Y location of the cg in the head frame, see Fig 2-1.
HW [gm] head weight (mass), weight of the head without shaft.	**Zcg** [in] Z location of the cg in the head frame, normally negative, see Fig 2-1.
LA [deg] loft angle.*	* More detail will be found for these items in the Appendix.
LAE [deg] effective LA, somewhat	

Golfer errors cause variations of HS which cause variations of bending, and therefore in LAE and FAE. That causes a small increase in the undesirable scatter of stop points. Accordingly, high shaft stiffness is important, especially for long hitters with drivers.

SHAFT WEIGHT

Shaft weight is also an important factor for distance with the maximum distance clubs (the driver and the first fairway wood). Shaft weight is of secondary concern for clubs other than the maximum distance clubs since any penalty in CHD caused by more shaft weight is easily compensated by choosing a longer club, as noted in several other chapters.

The loss of CHD for heavy shafts is because such shafts cause an unnecessary reduction of HS.

The lower 20 or 30% of the shaft is especially important, because it has a much larger effect on HS than weight high in the shaft. An approximation is to assume that a golfer can put about the same amount of kinetic energy into a club whether the shaft is relatively heavy or light. Thus, for a given CLG, a heavy shaft needs a lighter head if loss of HS is to be avoided. However, a lighter head gives lower CHD. During the very short time of impact, the shaft bends and, in effect, only the lower few inches participate in the impact, and the rest of the shaft's weight does not take part in the impact. This means that most of the shaft's weight is useless for transferring energy to the ball at impact.

To understand this better, imagine that 3 or 4 one pound weights are attached to the shaft at approximately equal spacing. The weights would slow your swing and HS would be much reduced. The lowest weight would slow HS much more than the upper weights. During the .0005 seconds of impact, the lower tip of the shaft would bend and the weights (particularly those higher on the shaft) would do almost nothing to help drive the ball. Shaft designers are aware of this and strive for light shafts.

Compared with graphite, most steel shafts have greater stiffness with correspondingly smaller variations of LAE and FAE due to variations of HS. Any loss of CHD is easily corrected by choosing a longer iron, but this option does not exist for the driver and first fairway wood. Steel shafts also have a small advantage due to higher torsional stiffness (commonly, but erroneously called "torque.")

These are the basic reasons why graphite shafts, being light and strong, are best for the maximum distance clubs whereas steel shafts, though heavier, are satisfactory or somewhat better for irons. Analysis shows that titanium, aluminum, fiberglass, and other materials have little or no advantage over steel shafts for irons. Thus, since steel has only a small advantage over other materials for irons, a golfer with a personal preference can use his preferred shaft material with confidence.

For drivers using CLG = 46 inches, Table 20-1 shows how increasing shaft weight reduces CHD. It was calculated for the BIGFACE 1 driver of our design which is similar to the "reference D driver." Other modern wood designs give similar results.

In each case, with shaft or grip weight different from the reference line (top line in each of the 2 groups), HW was maintained unchanged, the effect on HS was calculated, and optimum LA was calculated to best suit each new shaft and grip weight.

When we found and used the optimum HW for each change, the results are somewhat different from Table 20-1. Table 20-2 shows this result for a golfer midway between A and B. For each case, optimum HW, LA, and cg location were used, and the corresponding HS was also calculated and used. Table 20-2 is a better indication of the effects of shaft weight than is 20-1, for optimized clubhead design. The reason is that more shaft weight decreases the optimum HW and also, stores more kinetic energy in the shaft which is nearly useless for adding kinetic energy to the ball.

Note in Table 20-2 that the 40 gram shaft weights are essentially imaginary. Such light shafts of adequate strength are not available. The 80 gram shaft is typical of graphite and 120 gram, for steel. *Light shafts are an important advantage for maximum distance clubs of optimum design.*

The effect is independent of HCP and depends little on golfer strength and skill, as shown by the cases for high and low HS. Other HW and shaft lengths have similar results.

It may be concluded that if manufacturers could reduce shaft weight by another 10 grams or so, only about 1 yard can be gained in CHD. Such reductions are difficult to achieve if adequate shaft strength is to be realized. When CLG is changed, the situation is similar but more complicated, as discussed below.

Things such as bulges high up in the shaft, vibration frequency, high or low bend point (or kick point or flex point) have very different meanings from shaft stiffness, and have no direct relation to club performance. They tend to have an indirect relation inasmuch as they may be related to shaft stiffness and distribution of stiffness, but they do not substitute for stiffness and its distribution.

The shaft stiffness effects must be measured directly by such measurements as suggested in the previous chapter or by an equivalent means, rather than use of indirect or unrelated shaft characteristics. Figure 19-4 also shows that stiffness low in the shaft is what counts most.

In summary, our tests and theory indicate that for best performance, the driver shaft should be as light and stiff as possible, especially for 20 or 30% of the length and stiff at the tip end. It may be measured as discussed in Chapter 19. Driver stiffness is more important for golfers with high HS than for those with low HS. We believe that good current designs of graphite shafts perform very well. It appears difficult to significantly improve shaft designs for drivers and the first fairway woods over well-made current shafts which use good graphite materials.

Of course, a shaft must have adequate strength. Steel shafts are a good choice for irons.

Grip Weight

Grip weight is much less important than shaft weight. Refer to Table 20-1 for its effect. The lightest to the heaviest grip causes a gain in CHD of no more than about .5 yard. Grip weight is of little importance in the usual range of available grip weights.

Shaft Length for Drivers

Driver shafts are becoming longer. We believe this is

definitely the correct trend and that the common use of 46-inch CLG is about right. We studied this with some care by systematic tests of head speed with a wide variety of golfers.

For the test procedure, we made 9 test clubs with 88 gram, stiff graphite shafts, identical except for length; 3 had CLG of 43 inches, 3 had 46 inches, and 3 had 49 inches. For each length, 3 values were used for HW, namely 140, 170, and 200 grams.

Then, numerous golfers hit balls with these clubs with hit tapes on the faces. We found the size of hit patterns was reasonably independent of CLG and HW over most of the test range. Hit patterns were somewhat larger for the longest CLG and smallest HW; and also for the shortest CLG and smallest HW.

From among these, we arbitrarily designated the one with CLG = 43 inches and HW = 200 grams as our "reference T driver" and consider it to be representative of popular driver designs of about 1960 to 1980.

We measured HS on every swing. Our computer then found the MD which would result from perfect center hits under the condition that the LA and Ycg were optimum for each particular HS. In this way, results from our measurements became independent of whether or not the clubhead tested was well or poorly designed, whether or not the golfer had off-center hits, and other incidental effects such as wind. These are great complications for direct testing to find optimum CLG and HW.

Our next step was a curve fitting process. It showed the relation among MD, HW, and the shaft weight and length. It allowed calculation of the best combination.

We found that "ultimate design" for distance of drivers has a very light shaft and grip. Its length was 50.3 inches with 192 gram head, and this depended only a little on golfer size or skill level, male or female.

This was not a practical length for several reasons. We found that the size of the hit pattern increased somewhat for the 49-inch shafts and also for the 43-inch shafts with 140-gram head. Longer or shorter shafts and/or heavier or lighter heads reduced CHD. We believe more than about 46 or 48 inches is an inconvenience for a golfer in travel by car or in baggage, which is not justified by the small potential gain in CHD.

For a practical optimum CLG, we compromised by using a good, light, 46-inch shaft and 194-gram head weight, which was a little heavier than ideal for this shaft. This combination was close enough to provide CHD within a few yards of the ultimate.

We conclude that no driver design can gain more than about 2 yards over this practical compromise. We found that this applied about equally and with about the same loss of CHD relative to the "ultimate design" both for short and long hitters.

For drivers, it is interesting that for many years, CLG was almost always 42 inches, HW was about 210 grams, and the cg was much too high. In recent years, the truth is emerging and driver designs use more appropriate values, with 10 or even 20 yards gain in CHD. Our work indicates that such large gains cannot be expected in the future.

This also illustrates that the swing weight ideas were a poor approximation and probably don't serve much purpose.

Our model could readily compare CHD for specific early driver designs with modern designs which approach the upper limit of CHD. To do so for a specific golfer class requires measurements of the mass properties of the shaft and head (separately), and of the LA and FA.

Table 20-1 *The effects of driver shaft weight and grip weight on CHD for drivers for golfer P and golfer C. The top line in each group is a reference. Bold numbers are the changes of interest. The changes in CHD in the right column show significant gains for lighter shafts and little effect for grip weight.*

golfer type	shaft weight grams	grip weight grams	HS mph	CHD yards	change in CHD yards
P	69.7	43.5	118.73	284.13	0
P	**50**	43.5	119.86	285.90	+1.77
P	**90**	43.5	117.52	282.18	−1.95
P	**120**	43.5	115.55	278.90	−5.23
P	69.7	**30**	118.84	284.33	+.20
P	69.7	**70**	118.58	283.85	−.28
P	**0**	43.5	122.06	289.06	+4.93
P	**0**	**0**	122.19	289.29	+5.16
C	69.7	43.5	75.81	184.41	0
C	**50**	43.5	77.53	186.15	+1.74
C	**90**	43.5	76.01	182.41	−2.00
C	**120**	43.5	74.74	179.20	−5.21
C	69.7	**30**	76.86	184.55	+.14
C	69.7	**70**	76.70	184.09	−.32
C	**0**	43.5	78.95	189.37	+4.92
C	**0**	**0**	79.05	189.65	+5.24

Table 20-2 *The effects of driver shaft weight when the clubhead is fully optimized for each case (see text), for a golfer midway between A and B. Reference shaft weights (RSW column in the table) are for 46 inch shaft and actual weights are scaled up or down according to actual CLG. This result applies fairly well to all golfer classes.*

RSW, gram	CLG, in	HW, grams	CHD, yd	ΔCHD, yd
40	50	191.5	249.3	0.00
40	48	187.5	248.3	1.0
40	46	185.5	246.3	3.0
80	46	173.5	242.8	6.5
120	46	161.4	239.0	10.3

TECHNICAL NOTES

Our tests of the club length-head weight (CLG-HW) data on golfers are described above. Of the 9 test drivers, we used the one with CLG = 43 inches and HW = 200 grams as "reference T driver."

The test data gave for each golfer, the average HS for each of the 9 drivers. HS and HW (with the grip and same type of shaft as reference T driver), together with CA and SPA allow us to determine MD. From this we can determine MDr which is the ratio of MD of a given driver to that for the reference T driver.

We calculated another variable which we call MI and it is the moment of inertia of an individual test club about an axis perpendicular to the swing plane, 6.5 inches above, and 2.3 inches aft of the butt of the club. This is the typical location of the axis of rotation at impact for drivers. We calculated the ratio of this MI to a similar MI for reference T driver and called this ratio MIr, an important variable in our analysis.

We found that the MDr values could be expressed as a function of CLGr (ratio of CLG of the club to that of reference T club) and MIr. Since the results for all the golfers were similar, we determined the coefficients by expressing MDr as a generalized quadratic of the variables CLGr and the reciprocal of MIr by a least squares fit to all of the test data. The result is in good agreement with similar calculations we made, based on Reference 7.

From this surface, we found the combination for highest MD, namely CLG = 50.3 inches and HW = 192 grams; this depends little on golfer head speed, male or female.

Without this choice of variables, it would have been necessary to find a relation among LA, FA, club measurements Xcg, Ycg and Zcg, HW, HS, CLG, golfer variables, ball variables, and all the numerous atmospheric and terrain variables. The reason is that it is not obvious what effect one or more of these variables have on the optimum CLG-HW relation. With our analysis, effects of these variables can be studied separately from the CLG-HW problem.

If the testing had been done by directly measuring hit distance, experimental errors would have included all golfer errors, wind, etc. Worse yet is the problem that each hit would have been for a particular center of gravity (cg) and LA value, which generally would not have been closely suited for the particular HS.

Thus, each hit distance measurement would have included many effects other than the effects of CLG and HW and clear conclusions would have been obscured.

MD varies only slightly so long as CLG and HW are near the optimum. MD diminishes disproportionately faster for greater deviations from optimum.

We arbitrarily defined the "ultimate design" as a club having a hypothetical, extremely light weight shaft. This hypothetical shaft weighed 40 grams if measured at 48-inch length and its weight was increased in proportion to CLG. It is assumed to be lighter than can be achieved for any practical shaft. We assumed grip weight of only 20 grams.

From the calculations, we found that the above-mentioned optimum combination was length of 50.3 inches and head weight of 192 grams. This depended little on golfer size or skill level, male or female.

For our driver design work, we decided that a 70-gram, 46-inch long shaft is reasonably convenient and practical. We chose head weight of 194 grams which is a little larger than ideal for this CLG. It allows a large face size but still has adequate face strength for strong hitters. Hit patterns were not significantly enlarged with this choice of HW and CLG, but would be somewhat larger with much lighter HW and longer club length.

PERFORMANCE AND CHD RATING FOR DRIVERS

I F YOU THINK IT'S HARD TO DECIDE WHICH DRIVER DESIGN WILL GIVE YOU THE BEST SHOTS, HERE IS SOME SOUNDLY-BASED ADVICE FOR THE PROFESSIONAL AND THE NOVICE AS WELL.

CHOOSING A PERFORMANCE RATING

Chapter 6 introduced the subject of performance ratings for golf clubs. You may wish to review that chapter before reading this chapter. Here, we will elaborate on ratings for drivers and will include effects of POF hits.

Briefly, a defined performance rating is essential for optimizing a design and is useful to golfers to help judge which to choose from among the bewildering variety of drivers.

We use 2 reference drivers in this chapter, "reference T" and "reference D" driver (see definitions).

SYMBOLS AND DEFINITIONS	
AR [yd] accuracy rating for drivers which includes the effects of DE and ME.	error, measured from the stop point of an error-free center hit.
ARP [yd] same as AR except POF effects are included – MEP replaces ME.	**MEP** [yd] same as ME but effects of POF hits are included.
cg center of gravity.*	**POF hits** partly off the face hits for those hits near the edge of the face for which more than 25% of the imprint area would be off the face.
CHD [yd] center hit distance.*	
CLG [in] club length.*	
DE [yd] distance error, the distance by which a given driver's CHD stops short of CHD for a reference driver (usually reference D driver).*	**reference D driver** imaginary ultimate driver design having 40 gram shaft, CLG = 48 inches, 180 gram head, and 20 gram grip, design optimized for each HS in question.
dAA [deg] standard deviation of alignment angle.	
dHS [%] standard deviation of HS, expressed as %.	**reference T driver** a driver with 88 gram graphite shaft, CLG = 43 inches, HW = 200 grams, and 43.5 gram grip which we used in golfer tests and for frequent reference. Notice that modern drivers usually give up to 5 yards greater CHD than this reference.
dLA [in] standard deviation of long axis of hit pattern ellipse.*	
dSA [in] standard deviation of short axis of hit pattern ellipse.*	
golfers P, A, B, and C see Table 21-1.	
HCP handicap.	**UMD** [yd] ultimate maximum CHD with reference D driver for any particular golfer class.
HS [mph] head speed, speed of the cg of the head just prior to impact.	
LA [deg] loft angle.*	**Xstop** [yd] the X coordinate where the ball stops, measured in the fairway frame.
ME [yd] most probable error of stop points, taken to be the average	*More detail will be found for these items in the Appendix.*

DE is the amount by which a center hit for a given golfer class falls short of an ideal shot with *reference D driver* for the same golfer class when there are no golfer errors. DE is solely a function of club design. It is the same with or without POF effects, and is independent of HCP, because it is for center hits only.

For each driver in Tables 21-1, 21-2, 21-3, and 21-4, MEP and ME are the average errors (scatter) of stop points from each driver's center hit stop point, with and without considering POF hits. AR and ARP are accuracy ratings with and without POF hits, being the simple mean value of DE and ME or DE and MEP. Thus, AR is (DE+ME)/2 and ARP is (DE+MEP)/2.

SOME PERFORMANCE COMPARISONS

The tables compare the ratings of 6 driver designs for each of 4 golfer classes. Table 21-1 defines the 4 classes of golfers and Table 21-2 defines the 6 drivers in the other tables.

In all cases, we used the HS which each golfer class would have for the particular driver in question, based on shaft length and head weight research (Chapter 2 and 20).

We also assumed that a golfer would learn to adjust his grip and swing as necessary so that his ideal center hits (no golfer errors) are straight shots. Thus, we adjusted inputs for the straight shot condition for all drivers. This is discussed more fully in the Technical Notes. Accordingly, all 6 drivers are compared under optimum conditions of use for each situation, as a realistic basis for comparison.

Table 21-3 gives the resulting ARP ratings and deserves close study. The optimum driver for a particular golfer class is found by reading *across* each line to reveal how the various drivers compare. Reading down each column only shows the ARP for each golfer for that particular driver, not which driver is best for a particular golfer.

For example, the top line in the table shows that driver 1 is best suited for golfer P because it has the lowest ARP of all the drivers, for that golfer.

Similarly, the second and third lines show that driver 2 is best for golfers A and B; and line 4 shows that driver 3 is best for golfer C. This is as expected because we optimized the designs of drivers 1, 2, and 3 for respective center hit distances of 150-230, 220-270, and 260-300 yards.

Driver 4 is much worse, being a now-obsolete laminated wood design with its cg far too high, having low inertia values, and a rather small face.

Driver 5 has a rating representative of good drivers popular in about 1997. Driver 6 is progressively worse than driver 5 as HCP increases because its shallow face has many more POF hits for the higher HCP than does driver 5. Incidentally, it is also detrimental if the cg is too low, though few driver designs have this problem.

Table 21-4 gives more detail and makes it more clear how the various drivers result in the ratings given in Table 21-3. The first 5 columns are basic data on each driver, independent of POF. HS is the head speed which each golfer class would have for each particular club, and UMD relates to the ultimate maximum distance reached with the 180 gram, 48 inch reference D. It represents a hypothetical driver optimized for each golfer, but utopian in that it has a lighter shaft and head than is foreseeable for materials which would have adequate strength.

The CHD column is center hit distance and the DE column is the distance error which is UMD minus CHD. CHD and DE are independent of the POF effects.

Driver 1 gives lowest DE of all drivers for golfer P, a result of its optimized design for this golfer class and thus gives CHD several yards better than others. Driver 2 is best for golfers A and B. Driver 3 is best for golfer C. Driver 4 has a huge distance loss because of its very high cg and low moments of inertia. It shows clearly how much improvement has been made in golf club design in recent years.

Comparison of the ME and MEP columns show the extent to which scatter of stop points is increased by POF hits. POF hits show little or no effect for golfer P with zero HCP, and show progressively larger effects as HCP increases, becoming quite important for the higher HCP values.

Some Conclusions
About Performance Rating

We believe that ARP, or a similar rating for drivers, is meaningful to golfer and designer alike. Accordingly, it would be valuable as an industry standard, preferably promulgated by a respected neutral organization, though its administration would be difficult.

An additional conclusion comes from this research. CHD is more meaningful than LA as a basic reference in driver selection. This is because maximum distance is important to most golfers and LA alone doesn't define CHD because cg location and other things are very important.

As has been shown, for a given HS, CHD is related not only to LA but also to CLG, HW, and the cg location in the X, Y, and Z directions. Loft angle alone disregards these other factors, and thus can be rather misleading. Among club designs, the LA for optimum performance for a particular golfer HS may vary 2 degrees or more due to the other factors. CHD or a modest range of CHD provides an indication which avoids this and would be useful to golfers if manufacturers correctly determined the CHD and identified their drivers with it.

We have found that the entire range of golfer head speeds can be accommodated with only 3 CHD ranges. *More ranges would be needed for driver heads with poor cg location or lower moments of inertia.* Some golfers tend to hit higher or lower shots than usual. One reason is that they may have their hands unusually far rearward or forward at impact. For CHD ratings, they simply select the next range higher or lower.

For best comparison among drivers, golfers should consider both ARP and CHD ratings. Unfortunately, neither is generally available, but could be found by applying the research described here.

It is worthy of note that drivers 1, 2, and 3 are made of aluminum alloy and drivers 5 and 6 are of titanium alloy. The 2 metals have about equal suitability for the purpose. Titanium is light, strong, corrosion resistant and outstanding for high temperature uses. The latter 2 features are very important for aerospace uses but are unimportant for golf.

Aluminum is 58% as dense, so its face can be 72% thicker. The result is that aluminum can provide an equally strong face or even a little stronger for the same weight.

A GENERAL EXAMPLE OF
PERFORMANCE RATINGS AND DRIVER CHOICE

Now that we have discussed details of performance ratings here, in chapter 6, and other places, an example will help you further understand their meaning and uses. In a general example, we will use the basic idea that input errors cause output errors. Input errors include golfer errors, and deviations of the driver you are using from a hypothetical driver best suited for you.

Suppose you are a typical golfer, using an old-style driver such as driver 4, defined in Table 21-2. Your most important question is probably to know which items are of highest priority for improving your drives. You probably are approximately represented by one of the 4 golfer classes we've defined. For better accuracy, your principal errors could be measured, including dHS, dAA, and dWA but this is impractical.

Your hit pattern and other errors could also be measured, but they are usually less important when (as assumed) your driver is poorly designed. Driver 4 has cg much too high, CLG is too short, head weight may be too high, its inertia values are unnecessarily small, and it may not have LA which suits your needs.

In principal, your case could be run on our computer model. Likely, it would show that the most important items of all would be to lower cg, increase CLG, and adjust LA. This done, you would get much more CHD, and it would probably show that these changes are more important than trying to improve your technique.

Whether they are considered to be design errors, as compared to an ideal design for you, or merely design inputs, tends to be confusing. They do represent input errors in the sense they are deviations from an ideal design for you, so we classify them as design errors in this hypothetical example.

In any case, your largest gain would be to discard your driver and get one with design values reasonably near to what is ideal for you.

Suppose you do get a better driver. Now, your golfer errors may well become the most important input errors and anything you could do to aim better, control you head speed, etc., would be top priority.

Still, you may sometimes top the ball or hit partly under it (POF hits), or your new driver may have poor face shape, or inertia too low. Thus, you could try to find a still better driver with very large face to nearly eliminate the POF problem, large size to increase moments of inertia, and optimum face curvature to minimize effects of your hit pattern on scatter of shots.

After this, there is little left but to improve your game. You have found all that improved club design can do for you. Items such as your dAA, dHS, dWA, and the size of your hit pattern are the most important errors you can work on.

This is the logic behind choosing a better driver. If you happen to be using something like driver 4, a new one almost certainly is the first answer. This is not news to golfers, of course, and very few are using such old-style driver designs.

The problem now becomes one of finding out if your present driver is reasonably close to your needs or if you should try to find a better one. Some serious measurements of your errors and of your driver design would be excellent guidance, but that is almost prohibitively time-consuming and expensive.

The alternate is to try long drivers with light shafts, large faces, good face surface shape, and large heads. Use the one which gives you best CHD and fewest shots off the fairway (i.e., best accuracy, which means lowest ARP).

This can be a quick judgment, or for best results, may take a significant amount of practice and actual play with each of the more promising designs.

Table 21-1 *Definition of golfer classes.*

golfer P	HCP = 0, with HS = 114.1 mph, and CHD = 281 yards for reference T driver
golfer A	HCP = 10, with HS = 100.7 mph, and CHD = 251 yards for reference T driver
golfer B	HCP = 20, with HS = 87.2 mph, and CHD = 217 yards for reference T driver
golfer C	HCP = 27.5, with HS = 73.8 mph, and CHD = 179 yards for reference T driver

Table 21-2 *Definitions of the 6 drivers discussed here. Drivers 1, 2, and 3 are well optimized and are called BIGFACE 1.*

driver 1	our design for CHD 260-300 yards, 46 inch graphite shaft (Grafalloy Attack Lite shaft), HW = 191 grams, and 36 gram grip, **#1** designed for optimum CHD of 280 yards.
driver 2	our design for CHD 220-270 yards, 46 inch graphite shaft (Grafalloy Attack Lite shaft), HW = 191 grams, and 36 gram grip, **#2** designed for optimum CHD of 245 yards.
driver 3	our design for CHD 150-230 yards, 46 inch graphite shaft (Grafalloy Attack Lite shaft), HW = 196 grams, and 36 gram grip, **#3** designed for optimum CHD of 190 yards.
driver 4	a wooden head popular about 1980, 42 inch 80 gram graphite shaft, HW = 192 grams, and 43.5 gram grip, **#4** designed for optimum CHD (unknown).
driver 5	a representative large head driver of the late 1990s, 45 inch graphite shaft (Grafalloy Attack Lite), HW = 200 grams, and 36 gram grip, **#5** designed for optimum CHD of about 280 yards.
driver 6	a representative modern low profile head of 1999, 46 inch graphite shaft (Grafalloy Attack Lite), HW = 195 grams, and 36 gram grip, **#6** designed for optimum CHD of about 280 yards.

Table 21-3 *ARP, accuracy ratings with consideration to POF hits for the 6 drivers discussed here. On each line, the HS which was used was the actual HS which a golfer for each of the 4 golfer classes would have with the particular drivers in each column. Bold numbers identify the best choice for each golfer class.*

golfer	ARP [yds] for driver #s					
	1	**2**	**3**	**4**	**5**	**6**
P	**8.40**	9.58	12.18	29.71	11.08	12.18
A	17.64	**11.45**	13.08	37.32	14.70	21.70
B	13.69	**12.04**	12.60	41.83	17.36	28.13
C	14.60	11.92	**11.65**	40.43	18.52	29.52

Table 21-4 *Details of the component elements of accuracy ratings (yards) with no consideration of POF hits (ME and AR) and with allowance for POF hits (MEP and ARP) for the 6 driver types considered. See Technical Notes for explanation.*

golfer	HCP	HS mph	driver number	UMD	CHD	DE	ME	MEP	AR	ARP
P	0	118.30	1	289.37	285.59	3.78	13.02	13.02	8.40	**8.40**
P	0	118.30	2	289.37	283.18	6.19	12.96	12.97	9.57	9.58
P	0	118.30	3	289.37	277.78	11.59	12.78	12.78	12.18	12.18
P	0	114.10	4	289.37	249.92	41.45	17.96	17.96	29.71	29.71
P	0	116.77	5	289.37	281.33	8.04	14.07	14.13	11.06	11.08
P	0	118.45	6	289.37	280.70	8.67	14.13	15.68	11.40	12.18
A	10	104.38	1	262.55	255.66	6.89	16.17	16.38	11.53	11.64
A	10	104.38	2	262.55	256.03	6.52	16.32	16.38	11.42	**11.45**
A	10	104.38	3	262.55	253.10	9.45	16.67	16.72	13.06	13.08
A	10	100.70	4	262.55	214.27	48.28	25.98	26.35	37.13	37.32
A	10	103.06	5	262.55	253.08	9.47	18.27	19.92	13.87	14.70
A	10	104.54	6	262.55	248.16	14.39	21.47	29.00	17.93	21.70
B	20	90.46	1	228.80	219.23	9.57	16.73	17.81	13.15	13.69
B	20	90.46	2	228.80	222.14	6.66	17.04	17.42	11.85	**12.04**
B	20	90.46	3	228.80	221.67	7.13	17.76	18.06	12.44	12.60
B	20	87.20	4	228.80	175.62	53.18	28.87	30.48	41.02	41.83
B	20	89.24	5	228.80	217.26	11.54	20.03	23.19	15.78	17.36
B	20	90.52	6	228.80	209.13	19.67	26.07	36.59	22.87	28.13
C	27.5	76.55	1	190.19	177.43	12.76	14.97	16.45	13.86	14.60
C	27.5	76.55	2	190.19	182.03	8.16	14.93	15.67	11.54	11.92
C	27.5	76.55	3	190.19	183.56	6.63	15.88	16.67	11.26	**11.65**
C	27.5	73.80	4	190.19	136.58	53.61	25.21	27.25	39.41	40.43
C	27.5	75.53	5	190.19	175.47	14.72	18.93	22.33	16.82	18.52
C	27.5	76.61	6	190.19	166.32	23.87	25.29	35.18	24.58	29.52

TECHNICAL NOTES

Accuracy rating

We considered combining scatter and distance error, MEP or ME and DE by their product; square root of the product; mean value; square root of the sum of their squares (RSS); by differing weightings for each component in such combinations; etc. As either MEP or DE approach zero, we would not want one to cause a zero result in accuracy ratings, ARP (or AR) no matter how high the other, so a product is unsatisfactory.

RSS treatment will always cause the smaller of the 2 to lose its importance as it gets small and this seems undesirable. We could use a weighted mean, but it seems that, for example, a loss of distance of 10 yards would be about as offensive to a golfer as an increase of 10 yards in MEP. Either would be very disturbing and noticeable. The sum gives an unrealistically large result.

Accordingly, we decided to use the mean value. It is similar to what a golfer would notice in actual use.

In all cases, we used HS values derived from our basic club length-head weight (CLG-HW) relation so that the individual HS values are what golfers P, A, B, and C would have realized with the specified designs; and we used values for WA which give straight shots, and AA for Xstop near to zero.

Use of accuracy rating for driver choice

The above example of driver choice illustrates the problem. It is worth remembering that if our computerized model were used to guide a specific golfer, the driver must have its shaft removed to allow separate measurements of the head and shaft mass properties.

Also, the golfer's individual standard deviations of the common errors (dHS, dWA, dAA, dLA, and dSA) must be measured. It would remain to make the computer entries and run this case and perhaps examples for comparison with other drivers. Thus, detailed treatment for an individual golfer is not practical, but is practical for golfer classes such as the 4 classes we defined.

FAIRWAY WOODS AND IRONS

MUCH OF THIS WORK WAS FOR DRIVERS, HOWEVER, THIS CHAPTER SHOWS HOW MOST OF IT ALSO APPLIES TO THE FAIRWAY CLUBS. NOTE THE HELPFUL DIFFERENCES.

The previous chapters emphasize drivers and the first fairway wood. With minor modeling and program changes, they also apply to irons. In design of drivers and the first fairway wood, maximum distance and minimum scatter are both important. Thus for the performance rating, distance is a factor along with the scatter of stop points, in the same way as for drivers.

For irons and fairway woods, only scatter of stop points is important because a golfer can always choose a longer club if more distance is needed. Therefore the performance rating omits the distance error, DE, and considers only the scatter of stop points.

Drivers contact the ball when the club is about 1.7 degrees beyond straight down. We call this the contact angle, CA, and it is a program input. For non-drivers, we use CA = 0 degrees because the club is about straight down at impact.

Another difference is that irons are mainly used when the ball is expected to land on a green rather than on a fairway. Thus, bounce and roll (ZBR) calculation for irons is best chosen for greens rather than fairways.

POF hits are a different problem. Drivers use a tee, and thus, large variations of the hit pattern can cause POF hits off the top of the clubhead. This is not possible with fairway clubs because the bottom edge of the club normally digs into the grass and even into the ground before there is a POF hit off the top of the club face.

Exceptions are some of the very shallow face woods being promoted and also deep rough which holds the ball rather far above the ground. This means attention to toe-heel POF hits is important and ground clearance is also important. Thus, instead of hitting under the ball as with a driver, the problem with fairway clubs is hitting too far down into the ground, taking a divot before contact with the ball.

Effects of hitting off the toe or heel or topping the ball are calculated in the same way as for the drivers. As an approximation, the divot problem can cause very large errors in about the same way as POF hits off the bottom of a driver. If this is accepted, then the model works in the same way for fairway clubs as for drivers as regards POF hits.

Irons differ from fairway woods by having larger LA and also because the cg is forward and typically is in or near the face. For best results, they should have the cg rather low. For shorter irons, the cg cannot be put as low as optimum.

We have studied this briefly and it appears that for a wood more lofted than a 4 or 5 wood, this cg location problem begins to increase scatter and irons are therefore somewhat better for more lofted clubs, which agrees with the preference of most golfers.

Ideal face curvature becomes progressively less important as the loft increases and particularly, as the cg is nearer to the face. When the cg is in or very near the face, a flat surface above the ideal center hit location gives the least scatter of stop points. In this case,

SYMBOLS AND DEFINITIONS	
CA [deg] contact angle at the time of impact, positive when the cg is moving upward.*	imprint area would be off the face.
	reference D driver imaginary ultimate driver design having 40 gram shaft, CLG = 48 inches, 180 gram head, and 20 gram grip, design optimized for each HS in question.
cg [ ] center of gravity (more accurately, center of mass); its location is usually given in inches.	
DE [yd] distance error, the distance by which a given driver's shot stops short of CHD for reference D driver when HS is the same.*	**ZBR** [yd] bounce and roll distance for clubs other than putters, measured from where the ball hits down and the flight (carry) ends. See PD for putt distance.
LA loft angle.*	
POF hits partly off the face hits for those hits near the edge of the face for which more than 25% of the	* More detail will be found for these items in the Appendix.

curvature below the center hit location can be somewhat helpful to reduce scatter. This is included in one
of our pending patents.

High moments of inertia for the clubhead are
desirable to reduce scatter, particularly the moment
around a vertical axis. This agrees with the modern
trend to large-face irons.

We have designed fairway woods and irons
which use these ideas, but we have not yet done
extensive work on the mass distribution which minimizes scatter of stop points. We plan to do more
research when time permits.

Shafts for the longest fairway wood have about
the same consideration as for drivers in that
maximum CHD is an important consideration. Thus,
lightweight shafts are much preferred. For all other
fairway clubs, shaft weight is unimportant because
there is no need for maximum distance (a longer club
can always be selected if more distance is needed,
unlike the maximum distance clubs.) A result is that
lightweight shafts are not an advantage.

Steel shafts (which are heavier) also reduce twist
of the shaft because their torsional stiffness (so-called
"torque", a misnomer) is greater than graphite shafts.

We conclude that steel shafts are slightly better
for fairway clubs. This is consistent with preferences
of many or even most expert golfers. The difference
in scatter of stop points between steel and graphite is
small, so the choice of shaft material is not important.
The choice is mainly governed by golfer preference.

PITCH AND CHIP SHOTS

Perhaps the most important shots are those that demand you stop the ball near the hole. There is no such thing as "one swing fits all", nor the use of one favorite club.

Pitch and chip shots with partial swings are an important part of the game. Here, we use our computer model to show what happens for such shots with any of the various short irons.

It is often said that more strokes are wasted around the green than anywhere else on the golf course. Often a special situation happens when it is best to use a different club than the approach club which you usually prefer or you may be curious about what happens if you should change clubs. A good understanding of the distance of short shots is important for these reasons.

Figure 23-1 shows the distances for irons for shots which land on the green and bounce and roll, stopping on the green. The longer irons and woods extend these trends but we did not include them because shorter irons are used for most pitch and chip shots.

In Figure 23-1, the symbols show the distance which is usual for full swings with each of 5 clubs for each of the 4 golfer classes defined above (we call it FSD–full swing distance.) The part of each curve below a symbol is a partial swing for the golfer class represented by that symbol.

Figure 23-2 expands the data from Figure 23-1 for very short shots such as chip shots. Figure 23-2 applies to all golfer classes since the distances are much below the full-swing distances.

Very few golfers know their HS for partial swings and chip shots. These curves show the required HS for each of the indicated distances. Head speed is helpful because it is a good way to measure how hard you swing for such clubs as compared to the driver HS for your golfer class.

Even though you don't know your HS, you will be estimating the distance you want to achieve, and the figures give the corresponding HS needed.

These figures apply to normal golfing conditions with no wind and for greens in good condition which are reasonably flat and level; and they are for a normal swing. Such things vary, so variations must be expected from the calculations. The type of ball also somewhat affects the shots. The calculations apply to our reference ball.

The condition of the green can strongly affect the amount of the first bounce after the ball hits the green. The Stimp reading of the green has a strong effect on the roll distance. Bermuda grass may be somewhat different from the bent grass used in the model.

If an individual golfer does not have the average stance we modeled, or plays the ball unusually far forward or back in the stance, there is an effect on distance. Also, an individual golfer may have the hands more forward or rearward at the instant of impact than average.

These calculations are especially good for comparisons of various conditions. They apply for all classes of golfer. They are for good, well-maintained golf greens and for balls which land and stop on reasonably level greens.

For actual conditions, you must estimate corrections to the graphs in these figures for the effects of wind, hard or soft greens, slow or fast greens, greens which slope toward you, changes in your address from normal, and the type of ball you use. The graphs give basic guidance to the expected trends, and they are useful in spite of these limitations.

Figure 23-2 gives a good comparison of the various short clubs. The HS scale shows that for short shots such as 2 yards, you must swing a 60-degree wedge with a little more than twice the head speed as for a 40-degree 8 iron.

For longer shots, Figure 23-1 shows that the 8 iron goes about 2.5 to 3 times as far as the 60-degree wedge when both have the same HS.

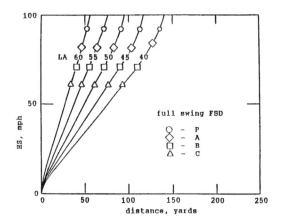

Fig. 23-1 *The relation between HS (head speed) and distance for various irons for shots which land on the green and stop there. The text gives the meanings of golfers P, A, B, and C. FSD means full swing distance.*

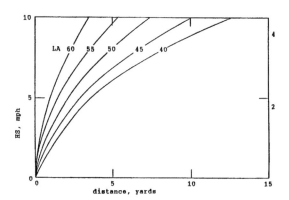

Fig. 23-2 *Expansion of Figure 23-1 for short distance and low HS. Golfer class does not apply for short distances.*

SPAN, THE UP-DOWN RANGE FOR GOOD HITS

WOULD YOU BELIEVE THAT USING A DRIVER COULD SOMETIMES BE PREFERABLE TO A WEDGE OR A SHORT IRON? WE DON'T RECOMMEND YOU DO SO IN EVERY CIRCUMSTANCE, BUT OUR MESSAGE IS CLEAR AND VERY BENEFICIAL. YOUR 9-IRON AND WEDGE, ESPECIALLY FROM TIGHT LIES, LEAVE LITTLE ROOM FOR ERROR. HERE ARE THE DETAILS.

SPAN H

This chapter is mainly concerned with clubs other than drivers and putters. Except for tee shots, when you hit too low, the bottom of your club strikes too far down into the ground (or soil); when you hit too high, you top the ball. It is important to know how much "span" (H) there is between too low and too high and to understand what makes span larger or smaller.

For H, when the clubhead is higher than ideal, we consider good hits to be those for which the ball imprint (ID) is entirely on the face or no more than 25% of the imprint area is off the bottom of the face. This is similar to our definition of hits partly off the face, described in Chapter 17. When the clubhead is lower than ideal, hits are good until the bottom of the club digs too deeply. The span is the difference between these upper and lower limits.

Figure 24-1 illustrates the span. For fairway hits from the grass (when no tee is used), H depends on a number of factors, but mainly on effective loft angle (LAE) and on the distance from the bottom of the ball to the soil (BG).

The span also depends on the bottom edge radius of the face (leading edge radius), on ID which is governed by LAE and HS, and on DD, which is the small distance the bottom of the clubhead may reasonably be allowed to dig into the earth. There is more detail on the calculation of H in the Technical Notes.

BALL-GROUND CLEARANCE AND H

Figure 24-2 shows how the grass holds the ball above the soil (earth). Our experiments showed that a downward force F of 1.3 pounds will press the ball down to the soil. It is difficult to see when the bottom of the ball actually reaches the soil, and we found that 1.3 pounds indicates the value of BG fairly well. More force causes the ball to begin to move down into the soil and leave an indentation. Small variation from 1.3 pounds does not significantly change the result. This test showed that BG = .35 inch for normal fairways.

Earlier, we tested actual hits on normal fairways with marking tape on the face of a club. These tests showed marks of soil beginning to be forced up the lower edge of the club face when the hit was low enough to dig into the soil. Marking tape on the club face located the center of the hit. That information allowed an independent calculation of BG; the average of these tests was also about .35 inch for normal fairways.

Table 24-1 gives the average result after 4 measurements for seven various kinds of grass. Grass in deep rough can hold the ball rather far above the soil,

SYMBOLS AND DEFINITIONS	
BG [in] clearance from bottom of the ball to the ground (the soil under the ball).	mph on our reference T driver and with HCP = 27.5.
CHD [yd] center hit distance, the distance of good center hits.*	**H** [in] span, the vertical distance from lowest to highest position of the clubhead for good shots.
DD [in] dig distance (distance the bottom of the face of a club digs into the soil.)	**HS** [mph] head speed.
golfer P a representative golfer with CHD = 281 yards and HS = 114.1 mph on our reference T driver and with HCP = 0.	**ID** [in] imprint diameter of a ball as it deforms against the club face, small for chip shots and progressively larger for strong hits.
golfer A a representative golfer with CHD = 251 yards and HS = 100.7 mph on our reference T driver and with HCP = 10.	**LA** [deg] loft angle.*
	LAE [deg] effective LA somewhat different from LA because shaft bending and other things alter head orientation.*
golfer B a representative golfer with CHD = 217 yards and HS = 87.2 mph on our reference T driver and with HCP = 20.	**Ych** [in] Y coordinate in the head frame of the ideal center of the hit pattern ellipse. For drivers, Ych = half the face depth (height) and for irons, Ych is different (see Technical Notes of Chapter 24.)
golfer C a representative golfer with CHD = 179 yards and HS = 73.8	*More detail will be found for these items in the Appendix.*

causing a large value of BG. In the damp areas of the short rough, the grass grows thicker and holds the ball higher than for normal short rough. Dry fairway grass has about the same BG as normal fairway grass. BG is much smaller on tees than on fairways and it is surprisingly small on putting greens.

We did little testing on deep rough because BG is usually very large and varies greatly. BG is zero on hard surfaces such as paths, paved areas, and hardpan.

BG is important for choosing the best club. You probably have a good idea about BG, but if in doubt, estimate BG by pressing down on a ball (not the ball in play) with a little over 1 pound of force to see how far down it moves.

If BG is small, you are likely to have better hits by using a club with less loft and an easy swing rather than a more-lofted club requiring a stronger swing.

When BG is large (in the rough, for example), a clubhead may even go completely under the ball, as most golfers know.

At the tee box, if you don't use a tee, BG may be only about 1/3rd as much as on the fairway, so more care is needed. Using a tee reduces or eliminates this problem.

On a typical putting green, BG is only about .04 inch, roughly the thickness of a paper match, and varies somewhat from this, depending on Stimp. When putting, it is important not to swing too low.

EXAMPLES

Table 24-2 shows that for a full swing on hardpan such as pavement, golfer A should not use a 7-iron or one with higher loft. A good hit is impossible because the imprint diameter is rather large and too much of the imprint will be off the bottom edge of the face even when there is no up-down error.

The problem is not quite so bad for golfers B and C because their imprint diameters are smaller. It shows that even ordinary tight lies allow very little up-down error and cause tight lies to be especially difficult when using highly lofted irons and a full swing.

For short distances, the swing is easy, HS is small, and this causes the imprint diameter to be small. Table 24-3 shows that for easy, partial swings, there is a reasonable up-down tolerance even for the highly lofted irons except on hardpan. These tables lead to the conclusion that on tight lies and hardpan,

the most lofted clubs should be avoided, as confirmed by the experience of many golfers.

Figure 24-3 illustrates the problem of hitting from hardpan with a highly lofted wedge. You can see at A that the imprint is slightly off the lower edge of the face for the 60 degree case. This is illustrated for edge radius of .04 inch which is typical. Larger edge radius makes it even worse. There is no tolerance for up-down hits and even with a perfect hit as is pictured in Figure 24-3, the imprint is partly off the bottom of the face.

The dotted line shows that using a club with much less loft greatly reduces the problem and allows a little up-down tolerance for the position of the clubhead at impact. Thus, a highly lofted club should be avoided for hardpan shots.

Hitting down on the ball by playing it back in the stance will increase H. This is because it effectively lowers LAE. We studied such cases and concluded the result is nearly the same as addressing the ball normally with a less lofted club. Playing the ball back may be useful in deep grass, but it doesn't help on hardpan.

SOLE SHAPE

Shape of the sole (bottom surface of the clubhead) seems to have only a small effect on H.

A V-shaped sole or a small radius causes less drag when the sole digs, but will throw dirt onto the club face and impair the hit, and may introduce trouble for hits which are not only low on the face but also somewhat toward toe or heel.

If the sole radius is too large, there is danger of the toe or heel dragging when the toe or heel end of the clubhead is too low. We concluded that most ordinary sole radii on clubs are reasonable and that there is no magic sole shape which significantly reduces the problem.

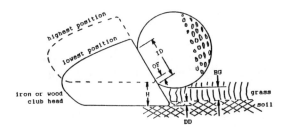

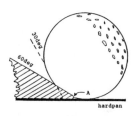

Fig. 24-1 *Illustration of span of up-down errors. H is the span. The grass holds the ball a distance BG above the soil. The club is allowed to dig into the soil an amount defined by distance DD. ID is the imprint diameter of the ball and OF defines the amount of the ball imprint which is allowed to be off the face.*

Fig. 24-3 *Illustration of the problem of using a wedge for hits from hardpan. You can see at "A" that the imprint is partly off the face with a 60 degree wedge, even with a perfect hit. The dotted line shows that a less lofted club such as 30 degrees eliminates the problem and allows good hits even when the clubhead is somewhat above the hardpan.*

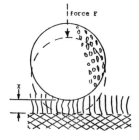

Fig. 24-2 *The ball is shown resting freely on the grass. A downward force F presses the ball farther into the grass as shown at X. BG is the value of X when F is 1.3 pounds.*

Table 24-1 *Ball-Ground distance, BG, for various kinds of grass.*

GRASS	BG, inches
short rough, damp area (bluegrass)	.861
short rough, normal (bluegrass)	.552
fairway, normal (bluegrass)	.346
tee (bentgrass)	.140
grass at margin of putting green (bluegrass)	.08 to .32
putting green (bentgrass)	.040
hard pan and pathways	.000

Table 24-2 *Up-down span H (inches) for good hits for golfers A, B, and C, for normal and for tight and hard (or hardpan) lies. Normal lies use BG=.35 and DD=.13. Tight lies use BG=.17 and DD=.08. Hard lies use BG=0 and DD=0.*

club	A golfer			B golfer			C golfer		
	normal	tight	hard	normal	tight	hard	normal	tight	hard
1W	.66	.49		.68	.48		.69	.49	
3W	.59	.40		.62	.43		.65	.46	
5W	.54	.34		.57	.37		.60	.40	
3I	.53	.33	.08	.56	.36		.59	.39	
5I	.45	.25	.02	.50	.29	.03	.53	.32	.08
7I	.38	.17	−.05	.43	.22	−.02	.46	.25	.01
9I	.32	.11	−.1	.39	.17	−.07	.41	.20	−.05
PW	.30	.08		.37	.15	−.08	.38	.17	−.07
SW	.27	.06		.35	.13		.36	.15	
W2	.25	.04		.33	.12	−.13	.34	.13	

Table 24-3 *Up-down span H for short distances (partial swings) for a few clubs. ID is much smaller than for full swings. The result is larger span. A, B, and C golfers all have the same result for these cases.*

club	loft deg	distance yards	imprint diameter inches	H, inches	
				fairway	hardpan
3I	23	10	.16	.78	.36
9I	46	10	.17	.51	.05
W2	60	10	.18	.40	−.06
3I	23	20	.24	.80	.32
9I	46	20	.25	.48	.04
W2	60	20	.26	.38	−.08
3I	23	30	.30	.73	.29
9I	46	30	.31	.47	.04
W2	60	30	.32	.36	−.10

TECHNICAL NOTES

We calculated span H using the equations below.

Here, in inches, RB is the radius of the ball, BG is the ball-ground distance, DD is the maximum acceptable dig distance into the soil, ID is the imprint diameter, and RE is the corner radius at the bottom edge of the club face. The last 2 equations define r and AD.

$$H = DD + BG + RB - r*\sin(LA) - .5*AD*\cos(LA) - RE*(1+\sin(LA)) \text{ [in], where}$$

$$ID = .9*(HS*\cos(LA)/85.6)^{.73} \text{ [in]},$$
$$r = SQR(RB^2 - .25*ID^2) \text{ [in], and}$$
$$AD = .4*ID \text{ [in]}.$$

The factor .4 in the equation for AD causes 25% of the imprint area to be off the bottom edge of the face. If more of the imprint is off, we estimate that the clubhead is too high for a reasonably good shot.

From our experimental measurements for fairways we used DD = .133 inch. DD is less for hard soil and zero for hard surfaces such as a paved sidewalk. RE is typically .03 to .06 inch. RB is .84 inch.

BG is measured as shown in Figure 24-2. ID is an empirical relation from our tests on the reference ball and may be slightly different for other balls. Remember that ID is small for short, easy hits and becomes much larger for strong hits.

These equations calculate H without considering that LAE is slightly different from LA due to shaft bending. We consider this small error to be negligible. It could be corrected in the equations with moderate additional complication.

Golfers minimize errors by centering hits midway in span H. This can be expressed as the desired vertical distance above the sole of the club which we call Ych. For all hits from the fairway, it is given by:

$$Ych = DD + BG + RB*(1-\sin(LA)) - H/2 \text{ [in]}$$

AIMING, HOOKS, AND SLICES

THIS CHAPTER GIVES A SIMPLE ANALYSIS OF THE CAUSE OF SLICES AND A SURE CURE FOR THEM, SOMETHING MANY TEACHING PROS SAY IS THE BIGGEST PROBLEM THEY SEE. THIS LED TO SOME NEW IDEAS ABOUT AIMING. YOU'LL FIND THIS VERY GRIPPING.

INTRODUCTION

In this chapter, we will refer to "hooks" and "slices" and will consider "draws" and "fades" to be simply mild versions of hooks and slices. As we will discuss in this chapter, flaws of aiming can cause unwanted hooks or slices. When you understand and control these "flaws", they allow you to generate draws and fades at will and the flaws become tools. The basis for this is side spin on the ball which we will discuss later. You needn't worry about side spin to learn to control hooks and slices.

The aiming process we suggest will give you easy control of hooks and slices. In addition, it improves accuracy for 3 reasons as follows. (1) There is a tangible gain because the aiming process doesn't require any alteration of your swing, which may be hard to repeat, may be somewhat uncomfortable, or may be hard to learn. (2) Specific things are listed for you to look at when aiming. (3) Perhaps most important is that your errors in taking the grip and your errors in alignment tend to cancel each other as discussed in the Technical Notes.

Figure 25-1 will help you understand the process.

Please notice that here we are concerned with all except very short shots. The aiming process for putters and short chip shots is quite different and is discussed in Chapter 32.

ADJUSTMENTS 1 AND 2, A NEW AIMING PROCEDURE

You can get improved accuracy by using 2 essential aiming adjustments. Adjustment 1 is to adjust your grip to give straight shots. Afterward, you make adjustment 2 to send these shots where you want them to go. These may be called "regripping" and "aligning", respectively. Here are these essentials:

1. Find the correct orientation of the club face with respect to the position of your hands on the grip, judged by looking at the club face and at the Vee's of your hands. Keep trying until you find the relative orientation which gives straight shots, not curving left or right. We call this "regripping." Don't worry if these shots are right or left of what you want – just worry about straight shots.
2. Take and adjust your stance to find the correct orientation of the club face, relative to where you want the straight shot to land, without regripping.

It is very important to make the 1st adjustment with no regard for the direction of your target. Only the club face and your hand position are important. It is also very important to make the 2nd adjustment without changing your grip. For the 2nd adjustment, you must rotate not only your feet, but your entire body (your stance). The 2nd adjustment is as if you stood on a turntable with its pivot at the ball and it was rotated as necessary to square the face relative to the direction you want.

Aiming errors are reduced in the regripping aiming process as stated in item 3 in the Introduction of this chapter. This is because the club face is used twice, once in adjustment 1 and again in adjustment 2, as explained further in the Technical Notes.

SYMBOLS AND DEFINITIONS	
AA [deg] the angle between the path of the clubhead at impact and the target direction, positive toward the left (more accurately, it is the angle between the target direction and the intersection of the swing plane with the horizontal plane,	positive to the left of the target.) **target direction** [deg] also called launch direction. It is the direction in which you want to launch the ball. **launch direction** see target direction.

Learning the 1st adjustment is best done by trial and error, making the face more closed relative to your hands to reduce slices and more open to reduce hooks, with no regard for the target direction. Learning the 2nd adjustment is also by trial and error with the turntable idea, but without regripping (that is, maintain the grip you selected in the 1st adjustment.) You align your stance after you have finished learning the first adjustment and adjust your stance until the shots go in the direction you want.

Depending on your habits, you may find that the best face orientation is slightly different among each of your various clubs. It appears that the adjustment for par 3 tee shots with clubs other than the driver, may also require a somewhat different face orientation than the same club used on the fairway.

The rest of this chapter is concerned with understanding how and why this aiming process works. It is not essential to learning the new aiming process, but will interest those who want to understand the basis. In particular, the following section describes 2 simple experiments which we urge you to make to familiarize yourself with these new aiming ideas.

AIMING EXPERIMENTS

Instead of the suggested regripping process, if you rotate (around the shaft axis) both your clubhead and wrists at address without taking a new grip, it has little effect on the orientation of the head at impact. You can make an easy experiment to convince yourself of this without even going to a golf course.

Experiment 1. Take your normal address position. Now rotate your hands and club together without taking a new grip until the club face is about 30 degrees open or closed. Slowly take your normal back swing. You find that your hands strongly tend to rotate back to their normal orientation or nearly so unless you modify your swing.

The following downswing also strongly tends to rotate your hands and wrists back to normal orientation if the back swing didn't do it completely. This puts the club face just before impact back to its normal orientation or nearly so, even though you started with the club face 30 degrees open or closed. Results are about the same if you make a normal swing instead of a slow swing but the swing will feel very awkward.

There is an easier way to change the face orientation just before impact and you need not change your swing. You turn the clubhead around the shaft axis to a new face orientation while keeping your normal address position of hands and eyes. Then take a new grip. The essential thing is that you have changed the angle between hands and the club face. Only the clubhead changes orientation; your hands and stance do not change position. We have not seen articles which recognize this fact and which explain it by experiments such as we suggest.

This leads to another convincing experiment you can try, either in slow motion as above or on actual hits on a course.

Experiment 2. Take your normal address position. Release your grip, orient the club face considerably closed, then take your grip again with the clubhead in the new orientation, but with your hands in their normal orientation. Now you have a new angle between your hands and the club face. When you take a slow swing and return to the address position, the swing feels easy and normal and the face stays closed.

The process gives a new club face orientation. We call this regripping because you take a new grip with the face at the desired orientation relative to your hands.

Notice also that this method of changing club face orientation has no effect on your normal swing because your hands are always in their normal position. If you would like more technical detail, refer to Figure 25-4, which shows the main things to observe when regripping.

THE CAUSE OF HOOKS AND SLICES

One of the essentials of good aiming is to avoid hooks or slices. Here we will explain slices in terms consistent with what many golfers know. Hooks are simply the reverse situation. Also, left-handed golfers must reverse things appropriately.

Figure 25-2 illustrates the fundamentals for center hits with no wind. The sole cause of hooks or slices for center hits is side spin, and side spin happens when the club face is not square to the swing path at impact. Side spin causes a lateral force on the ball during its flight for well-known aerodynamic reasons, and this force curves the shot. Note that in the figure, the target direction is not shown. Contrary to common belief, the target direction should not be used as a reference to orient the face to the swing path. When the face is square to the swing path, there is essentially no side spin. The shot will be straight. This is true for an outside-in swing, a perfect swing, or an inside-out swing.

Case A in Figure 25-2 shows a typical outside-in swing, with the face not square to the swing path. It results in side spin and a curved shot (exaggerated in the figure.) Case B shows the club face reoriented to be square with the path, and the shot is straight, but the alignment needs to be changed as discussed elsewhere in this chapter.

Hits which are off center toward toe or heel are a different matter. They also cause side spin and give curved shots. Proper curvature of the face surface minimizes errors for such hits. Face curvature was discussed at length in Chapter 18.

DISCUSSION

In our design work with drivers, we were concerned with minimizing the common tendency to slice. This led to the methods and experiments described in this chapter regarding ways to aim. These suggestions give straight shots on average whether your swing is good or bad, outside-in, or inside-out. We do not mean to suggest that these new ideas are a substitute for learning a good swing and a good grip.

Figure 25-1 illustrates 3 different face orientations, as viewed by a golfer. B represents what is conventionally thought of as an ideal orientation. At A, the face orientation illustrates the correct direction for you to reorient the face (as compared with B) when you want to reduce a slice or to cause a hook. The opposite reorientation at C reduces hooks or causes slices.

As explained in the previous section, shots hook or slice (draw or fade) when the club face is somewhat closed or open relative to the clubhead path just before impact regardless of the reason why it is closed or open.

An outside-in swing path is common among golfers. It usually is accompanied by the club face being open at impact. This is because the path is generally left of where the golfer wants the ball to go, so the tendency is to compensate by having the club face more open. This causes a slice. Even a swing which is severely outside-in will give a straight shot if the face is square to the path just before impact but

the ball will fly to the left. Proper club face orientation deserves great attention and is the most important aspect of aiming.

We have discussed adjusting the face orientation and then regripping. This has the interesting consequence that it does not matter what "face angle" may be built into your clubs. If you imagine a super-closed face, for example, when this face is aligned appropriately with respect to your hands, the face angle does not matter. Similarly, face progression and shaft progression are not factors when you use the suggested regripping procedure.

Remember that by suggesting regripping, we don't mean to change the way you grip the club. We do mean to adjust the clubhead orientation properly relative to your hands before you take your grip. It is your same, normal, comfortable grip. Don't change your backswing or downswing in any way.

Regripping has the same effect as the usual instruction to change the position of the Vee of your hand, provided you do not change orientation of the clubhead when you change the position of the Vee. This latter point is often not mentioned in conventional instruction about strong and weak grips, but it is essential to controlling of hooks and slices. We suggest that reorienting the clubhead rather than reorienting the position of your hands (changing the Vee) is more comfortable and more effective.

As an extreme example, you could not comfortably make a 90-degree change by changing the Vee, but it is easy by reorienting the face. There is no physical reason why regripping should alter the feel of the swing because there is no change in position of the body, hands, wrists, or arms.

In contrast, changing the Vee gives many golfers a different feel for the swing. This is detrimental because a good golfer wants to feel a "grooved" swing which never changes. See the Technical Notes for more detail.

In summary, the sequence for aiming is: first, to get straight shots, choose the appropriate club face orientation with respect to your hands, with no regard for the target direction, then take your grip; second, without changing your grip, choose the appropriate club face orientation relative to the direction you want by adjusting your stance (the turntable idea) as required.

HOW A SLICE CAN GET PROGRESSIVELY WORSE

Some ideas about aiming may lead you to take your stance and square the club face to the target or do this in reverse order. If you do this and have a persistent slice, you are likely to align your stance more to the left. This causes the line of travel of the clubhead to be more toward the left. Now if you square the face to the target before gripping, it is even more open with respect to the line of travel of the clubhead just before impact and the slice is worse. More adjustment of this type causes even more slice. The reverse can affect hooks similarly.

This illustrates that the target should not be used for orienting the club face when regripping. This is central to our new suggestions for aiming.

COMPARISON OF THE IMPORTANCE OF ERRORS IN ADJUSTMENTS 1 AND 2

This chapter's 2nd section explained adjustment 1 as finding the correct angular orientation of the club face relative to your hands. Adjustment 2 was to properly adjust the club face orientation without regripping by changing alignment. Inevitably you will have errors in making these 2 adjustments. These are the 2 errors we will consider in this section.

Our model shows results of these 2 errors in clubhead orientation. We consider adjustment 1 first. For center hits with drivers, a golfer who hits 250 yards has a lateral error of about 22 yards if the face is oriented 2 degrees too far open or closed at impact, as compared to club face orientation which is square to the direction of travel of the clubhead. A golfer who hits 220 yards makes lateral errors of 16 yards and a golfer who hits 180 yards makes lateral errors of 11 yards. That is, the lateral error increases progressively faster with distance of the hit. It is a small concern with short hitters and a large concern for long hitters.

By comparison with adjustment 2, the corresponding lateral errors due to 2 degrees alignment error for these 3 cases are 8.7, 7.7, and 6.3 yards.

Thus for the 3 cases, adjustment 1 is 2 to 3 times as important as adjustment 2.

For the longer irons, such as the 6-iron or 5-iron or longer, similar calculations show that adjustment 1 is about 2 times as important as adjustment 2. For the 9-iron and the wedges, they are about equally important.

VISIBILITY OF ERRORS

The previous section showed that rather large errors can be caused by small errors of orientation of the club face. You must be especially careful about making adjustment 1 correctly for the driver and the longer clubs. This is mainly because adjustment 1 alters side spin. For the short irons, side spin has a much smaller effect on lateral errors and the adjustments are about equally important.

These 2-degree changes in club face orientation are illustrated in Figure 25-3. The 2-degree change is hard to see. This shows that you should observe the face orientation very carefully when aiming.

We have made experiments which show that golfers maintain club face orientation more accurately with a very large club face rather than a small one, another advantage for clubs having large faces. Since correct club face orientation is very important, anything which can reduce orientation errors is worth serious attention.

Figure 25-1 shows a good way to judge club face orientation. Without regard for the target direction, look at your hands, your feet, and the shaft axis so you are sure that all appear in what you consider to be their usual and normal address positions before you worry about the club face orientation. Adjust the face orientation after checking that these other angles are normal by adjusting the face orientation shown in Figure 25-1. The face orientation at A tends toward hooks and at C, toward slices. Regrip after you have chosen the face orientation. The shaft axis is a very useful reference for making these judgements. Notice that the face and the Vee are nearly parallel to the shaft, and thus reasonably easy to judge.

Use of the shaft axis to help find the right orientation of the club face apparently is seldom used by golfers. Your hands, shaft, and club face are right there in your field of view, and are easy to judge. Figure 25-1 should help you understand these angles and guide you to observing that the angle between the face and the shaft axis is what you want and that the other angles are normal for your swing. After practice, this can be done with little special attention. The shaft axis is not essential to good choice of the club face angle, but we believe that many will find it helpful.

Always remember that orientation of the club face relative to the hands is normally the most important factor for best accuracy, whether or not you use the shaft axis as part of the aiming process.

This club face orientation method can be done before or after you step to the ball to choose your alignment. In any case, be sure to choose club face orientation relative to your hands rather than to the target.

Many golfers simply depend on their instincts to have the correct orientation of their hands and body and may do very well without consciously looking.

We believe that most golfers look at the club face when they choose clubhead orientation, probably unconsciously. Other features of most clubhead designs do not indicate club face orientation very well.

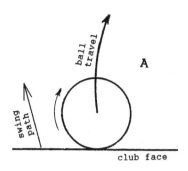

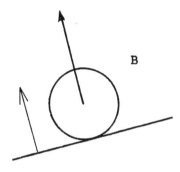

Fig. 25-2 *The cause of slices for center hits. Case A shows a typical outside-in swing path with the face open relative to the swing path direction. This causes a slice. Case B shows an outside-in swing path but with the face square to the swing path, causing a straight shot. Shots have almost no curvature when the face is square to the swing path.*

A   B   C

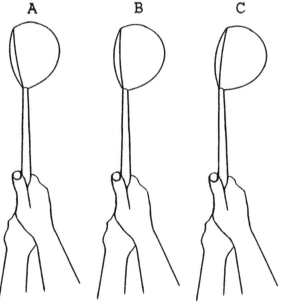

Fig. 25-1 *Adjustment of clubhead to control slices and hooks. Notice that orientation of the hands does not change, whereas the face orientation does change. In this process, the grip is released, the head is readjusted, and then the same grip is taken again. Slices are suppressed by the head orientation shown at A; hooks are suppressed at C. Target direction is not a factor in this adjustment. Figure 25-4 gives more detail. This replaces the conventional "strong" and "weak" grip procedure.*

Fig. 25-3 *The left clubhead is oriented 2 degrees closed, the center one is square, and the right one is 2 degrees open. These small changes are hard to see but they cause lateral errors of 20 yards or more with a driver. Great care is needed when aiming.*

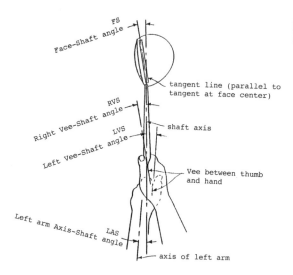

Fig. 25-4 *A suggested way to choose clubhead orientation. The tangent line can be absent and the club face used instead. First, make sure LAS, LVS, and RVS are ok and normal, then adjust FS to the position you prefer and then take your grip. We call this regripping. All these angles are nearly zero. FS is the angle which a golfer should adjust to control hooks and slices.*

TECHNICAL NOTES

Figure 25-4 repeats the message of Figure 25-1 in more technical form and labels the important angles.

Reference 1, page 90, partly confirms our basic comments about regripping by indicating that the angular position of the wrists is driven by the dynamics of the swing, rather than the angular position of the wrists at address controlling the dynamics of the swing. We suggest that the angular position is probably governed more by static factors, as demonstrated by the slow swing experiments suggested above.

Centrifugal force is probably also a significant factor. Considering centrifugal force up to 100 pounds, it is reasonable to expect that this force tends strongly to put the wrists into their normal orientation.

How regripping reduces combined aiming errors

At the beginning of this chapter, we said that using the face as a reference for both adjustment 1 and for adjustment 2 reduced aiming errors. That is because using the face twice makes adjustments 1 and 2 interdependent. An error made in adjustment 1 is present when adjustment 2 is made. When adjustment 2 is made from this erroneous face orientation, the result is more likely to reduce the error of the first adjustment than to increase it, without any tendency to increase the error made in adjustment 2.

If you study this process carefully, you can see that if your clubhead orientation is normally different at impact from what it was at address, the process properly allows for this difference. That means this difference is something you need not worry about.

Not discussed above, a small amount of side spin is caused by the rotation speed of the head around the shaft axis at impact. This is included in our model, but it is a minor effect in connection with this discussion.

EFFECTS OF BALL DESIGN VARIABLES

DO YOU FIND THE DIFFERENCES IN WEIGHT AND SIZE AND PROMOTIONAL PROMISES CONFUSING? THESE AND OTHER IMPORTANT FACTORS REGARDING PERFORMANCE ARE EXPLAINED.

A great deal of research on golf balls has been done, and some is included in some chapters of References 4, 5, and 6. Nearly all of our research was based on a single ball which we call the "reference ball", defined in the Symbols and Definitions box below. The computer model allows variation of many of the basic characteristics of balls, and we will describe a few of the calculated effects for the principal ball design variables.

The United States Golf Association (USGA) has set limits for balls on maximum weight (1.62 ounces), minimum diameter (1.68 inches), spherical symmetry, initial velocity, and overall distance. Most balls are designed to be very near these limits.

Manufacturers have studied variations in the dimple pattern, how well a ball bounces, the nature of its cover, the distribution of mass somewhat more toward the center or toward the surface (thus varying the principal moment of inertia), and other factors.

We will show the effects of changing ball variables individually. A very large number of combinations is possible when 2 or more variables are changed simultaneously. We did not take the space to show these combinations, though the model will easily do so.

We also made no attempt to determine optimum combinations or design improvements as we did for golf clubs. This information is presented only to show the trends.

Possibly more could be learned about optimum ball design by use of our model with a complete study of the effects of various combinations of these variables on distance and scatter of golf shots.

Table 26-1 shows the main characteristics of center hits for the ball, used for nearly all the calculations in this book. These are for normal golfing conditions, flat greens (or fairways for the 1 wood), and no wind. The drivers in these examples are our optimized driver design marked 1w and the 5 and 9 irons representative of modern large-face irons. This table is the reference set of ball flight results to which the following 3 tables are compared.

Tables 26-2, 26-3, and 26-4 show how a center hit is affected by the changes indicated in the first column for ball design variables with golfers P and C. The biggest effect is 10% increase in diameter, which causes about 20 to 30 yard loss of CHD for golfer P. Had we reduced Db, there would have been a large gain in CHD. Ball weight has a rather large effect. NCR and Cd are also important. The tables show that ZBR and the height are affected relatively little by changes of the ball design.

Remember that some of these results, while accurate, require interpretation. For example, if Db is

---

SYMBOLS AND DEFINITIONS

Cd [] aerodynamic drag coefficient of the ball.

CHD [yd] center hit distance.*

Cl [] aerodynamic lift coefficient of the ball.

Db [in] diameter of the ball.

golfer P a representative golfer with CHD = 281 yards and HS = 114.1 mph on our reference T driver and with HCP = 0.

golfer C a representative golfer with CHD = 179 yards and HS = 73.8 mph on our reference T driver and with HCP = 27.5.

H [in] span, the vertical distance from lowest to highest position of the clubhead for good shots.

HS [mph] head speed, speed of the cg of the head at the time of impact.

ID [in] diameter of imprint of a ball on the club face.

Mb [lbf*in^2] moment of inertia of the ball.

NCR [] coefficient of restitution for normal impulses.

POF hits partly off the face hits for those hits near the edge of the face which more than 25% of the imprint area is off the face.

reference ball we used a ball which was popular a few years ago for all impact results, the Dunlop DDhII. In some other tests, we used a Spalding Top Flight Plus II as noted.

Sr [rps/sec] rate at which the ball is spinning.

SCR [] coefficient of restitution for shear impulses.

Wb weight of the ball.

ZBR [yd] bounce and roll distance for clubs other than putters, measured from where the ball hits down and the flight (carry) ends.*

(Also, see special variables listed in this chapter.)

* *More detail will be found for these items in the Appendix.*

changed, the model could be used to determine optimum loft angle and center of gravity (cg) location for the new ball size, which might or might not somewhat alter the calculated effect of changing Db. Furthermore, weight of the ball is likely to change if Db changes, and other characteristics may change. The tables assume no changes were made other than in the listed items.

For good reasons, USGA Rules of Golf control performance of balls which meet their standards in such a way that little or nothing can be gained in CHD by altering the ball design variables which govern CHD.

Table 26-1 *Values of NCR, SCR, Cl and Cd for center hits. Cl and Cd are values at launch. In addition to the ball variables given in the table, we used Db = 1.68 inches, Wb = 1.62 oz, and Mb = .0225 lbf∗in∧2.*

golfer	club	inputs					results, yards		
		HS, mph	NCR	SCR	Cl	Cd	height	ZBR	CHD
P	1w	119.0	.735	−.276	.165	.261	32.9	28.9	285.9
C	1w	75.5	.797	−.236	.199	.260	13.8	37.4	182.4
P	5i	98.9	.770	−.332	.216	.266	47.2	15.0	220.1
C	5i	64.0	.818	−.278	.226	.274	17.1	20.9	139.4
P	9i	93.1	.800	−.404	.285	.291	52.2	6.8	141.2
C	9i	60.2	.838	−.333	.294	.313	21.8	8.5	92.3

Table 26-2 *Effects of changes in ball characteristics from those of Table 26-1 on center hits for an 1 wood of optimized design.*

change of variable	golfer P			golfer C		
	height	ZBR	CHD	height	ZBR	CHD
Db+10%	+3.6	−7.6	-29.7	+2.1	−7.7	−10.0
Wb+10%	−4.2	+4.7	+6.5	−1.3	+3.6	−1.2
Mb*+10%	−1.7	+.6	.0	−.3	+.5	−.3
Sr+.05	−.3	−.3	+1.4	+1.3	−.3	+.8
NCR+.05	+2.3	−.9	+7.1	+1.2	−.7	+6.6
SCR+.05	+.7	−.6	−.2	+.1	−.3	+.1
Cl+10%	+3.8	−2.6	+4.2	+1.8	−1.9	+4.1
Cd+10%	−3.6	−1.2	−18.3	−.6	−1.6	−8.6

Table 26-3 *Effects of changes in ball characteristics from those of Table 26-1 on center hits for a 5 iron.*

change of variable	golfer P			golfer C		
	height	ZBR	CHD	height	ZBR	CHD
Db+10%	+3.2	−4.6	−25.4	+1.8	−5.6	−8.7
Wb+10%	−2.6	+2.7	+9.5	−1.0	+2.4	+.1
Mb*+10%	−.8	+.5	+3.3	−.3	+.5	+.2
Sr+.05	+.6	−1.7	+.3	+.1	−.9	−.4
NCR+.05	+2.8	−.2	+7.9	+1.2	.0	+5.5
SCR+.05	+.5	−.7	+1.8	.0	−.5	−.5
Cl+10%	+3.7	−.4	+2.5	+1.0	−.8	+2.1
Cd+10%	−2.8	−1.9	−11.8	−.5	−1.8	−6.5

Table 26-4 *Effects of changes in ball characteristics from those of Table 26-1 on center hits for a 9 iron.*

change of variable	changes in results, yards					
	golfer P			golfer C		
	height	ZBR	CHD	height	ZBR	CHD
Db+10%	+.7	−2.0	−21.5	+1.0	−2.4	−7.8
Wb+10%	−1.4	+1.0	+5.2	−.8	+.8	+.2
Mb*+10%	−.5	+.4	+2.3	−.3	+.4	+.8
Sr+.05	+.2	−1.4	−2.2	+.1	−.8	−.8
NCR+.05	+2.9	.0	+3.6	+1.3	+.1	+3.5
SCR+.05	.0	−.5	−2.0	−.1	−.3	−.5
Cl+10%	+2.1	+.2	−1.9	+.7	−.1	+.4
Cd+10%	+2.3	−1.2	−7.7	−.5	−.9	−3.8

TECHNICAL NOTES ·

We have made no effort to study the ball design in more detail than shown in the tables. Of particular interest would be how the ball may affect scatter of hits. More refined calculations may be practical for how spin decays with ball velocity or how other variables achieve different results. The model would facilitate such work for all or most of a ball's basic design variables.

We allowed for variation of NCR and SCR as follows where the impulse is in [lbf*sec]:

NCR = .913 − .000604 * normal impulse [ ]

SCR = −.155 − .0165 * shear impulse [ ]

As part of our testing, we used marking tape on the club face for many hits with drivers and various irons. All of these marking tapes showed dimple patterns of the ball with rare evidence of sliding. Several years ago, USGA made careful tests in connection with the importance of grooves in a club face, and also found little evidence of sliding. This led us to describe the dynamic behavior of the shear impulse as a simple shear coefficient of restitution, SCR. Further, we found that the value used for SCR had only a small effect on results as shown in Table 26-2. We chose a value which gave results consistent with golfer experience.

Impact diameter (ID) varies with the design of the ball and with the severity of the impact, i.e., with speed of the clubhead.

The model calculates ID as given in the Technical Notes of Chapter 24. More rigid or softer balls would have slightly smaller or larger values for ID, but we suspect effects would be small.

A harder ball of the standard diameter has a smaller ID and this increases the up-down span (H). Smaller ID and larger H would be somewhat advantageous with respect to POF hits. (H was discussed in Chapter 24.)

For Cl and Cd, we approximated graphs by Aoyama in Reference 15 by the equations for Cl and Cd given below.

$$Cd = Cd1 + Cd2*Xv + Cd3*Yv + Cd4*Xv*Yv + Cd5*Xv*Xv + Cd6*Yv*Yv; \text{ and}$$

$$Cl = Cl1 + Cl2*Xv + Cl3*Yv + Cl4*Xv*Yv + Cl5*Xv*Xv + Cl6*Yv*Yv; \text{ where}$$

the Cd coefficients, in the above order are:

.2320, .3060, .03678, −1.719, −.1182, and 1.467;

the Cl coefficients are:

.1330, .6530, −.0986, .5899, −.2290, and −1.1344;

$Xv = (\text{Reynolds No} − 10^5)/10^6$;

$Yv = (\text{PSB})/(\text{RSB})$; where

RSB means speed of the ball's center relative to the surrounding air mass; and

PSB means the equatorial peripheral speed of the ball surface due to spin alone, when we neglect the component of spin which is parallel to the ball velocity vector relative to the surrounding air mass.

We expressed the rate at which the ball spin decreases as:

$Sr/Sr0 = e^{(−t/k)}$, where

Sr is the spin rate at time t, Sr0 is the initial spin rate, and k is the time constant for the rate of decay of the spin. We found that k = 20 seconds agreed reasonably well with the data in Reference 4, pages 225-230.

Refinements in these measured characteristics of golf balls are reported in References 5 and 6 which had not yet been published when we did this part of our work. We expect such refinements would have little effect on the trends and conclusions we have reported and as indicated in the tables above.

Part Four

PUTTERS

THE MODEL AND OUR RESEARCH ON PUTTERS

THE SUCCESS OF A PUTT IS MORE SENSITIVE TO SMALL LATERAL ERRORS THAN TO SMALL DISTANCE ERRORS. WE STUDY SWING PATH DIRECTION, CLUB FACE DIRECTION, OFF-CENTER HITS, CENTER OF GRAVITY, HEAD SPEED, INERTIA VARIABLES, AND WEIGHT. IT ALL STRIKES HOME.

PUTTER MODELS

We applied the same research methods to the design of putters as we used for woods and irons, using certain modifications of our model.

Figure 27-1 is a top view of putter impact and illustrates our model and a few of its many inputs as used for putters. The principal difference was replacing the flight portion of the ball's travel with a calculation which ignores air drag on the ball, justified by the low speed. Following this simplified short flight, friction of sliding on the grass causes the ball to start rolling and increases the rate of roll until the ball begins to roll without slip. Finally the ball rolls without slip from there to the stop point, governed by equations we derived from many measurements of roll on actual greens.

The Technical Notes give these equations for the putt distance model. We considered only flat, horizontal greens.

Golfer experience agrees reasonably well with results of this model. Results for actual greens differ when the effects of slope of the green are present, as golfers know.

The putter adaptation of our general model gives the same advantages for putter designs as for driver and iron designs. It allows the designer to avoid the great variety of experimental errors involved when making tests of designs with actual golfers and allows design variations to be evaluated quickly. The effects of even very small variations can be studied with good precision. The effects of variations are difficult or impractical to measure directly by testing because they are masked by variations in turf and other experimental errors.

ERRORS

Figure 27-1 also explains the principal angular errors made in putting as standard deviations in alignment angle (dAA) and in club face direction (dTA). Most golfers try to avoid rotation of the wrists and putter head during the swing which suppresses variations of wrist angle. Any wrist angle changes are part of dAA and dTA, and the latter also include golfer errors in correctly judging intended direction of the putt for level greens. The results could be somewhat improved by direct measurements of dTA and dAA as will be discussed in Chapter 29.

At address when putting, golfers generally should try to adjust the clubhead so that the face is square to the target direction which means they should try to minimize TA. They should then take their grip with this orientation. We believe this is what most golfers actually do when putting. This is discussed at length in Chapter 32.

The ball may be hit off center by some amount such as shown at x in Figure 27-1 and it may also be too high or too low on the face. The model shows that these 2 errors cause nearly negligible effects on the stop point (unlike off-center hits for other clubs).

For putts expected to break, the target direction

SYMBOLS AND DEFINITIONS	
AA alignment angle.*	**dTA** [deg] standard deviation of TA.
cg [] center of gravity (more accurately, center of mass); its location is usually given in inches.	**HS** [mph] head speed.*
	PD [ft] total distance of a putt.
	S [ft] Stimp reading which is the distance a ball rolls on grass after rolling freely down a specified ramp.*
dAA [deg] standard deviation of AA.	
dHS [%] standard deviation of HS just before impact as a percent of HS.	
dLA [in] the standard deviation of the center of impact locations (hit patterns) on the club face, measured in the direction of the long axis of the impact pattern. dLA is approximately in the toe-heel direction.	**TA** [deg] target angle for putters. See also "target direction" and Figure 27-1.*
	target direction [deg] also called launch direction. It is the direction in which you want to launch the ball.
dR [ft] standard deviation of putt distance with all errors present.	* More detail will be found for these items in the Appendix.

is different from the hole direction. Good golfers probably judge this difference considerably better than poorer golfers. Our analysis does not consider this judgement factor.

A number of inputs for the head include its weight, inertia variables, cg location, and head speed. Inputs also include golfer errors, green errors, the main characteristics of the ball, and S (the Stimp reading).

The stop point of the ball is the most important output because it allows calculation of the success of the putt. For successful putts, the stop point is such as to make the putt drop, which will be discussed in detail later.

The program can automatically vary the position of hits on the face and other golfer errors with the same statistical distribution as happens for actual golfers and calculate such things as the corresponding scatter of stop points and the success of putting.

RESEARCH AND TESTING

Our laboratory putting machine is large and sturdy with means for precisely adjusting the impact point. The ball is on a long string as a pendulum, and mounted so that every hit is made at exactly the same spot on the ball. We used a video camera to track ball motion. From this, we calculated where it would stop if on a perfect green (actual, imperfect greens are discussed later). This machine permits precise evaluation of off-center hits, but gives no indication of effects of other putting errors. Most of our conclusions are based on other tests and calculations with our model.

We made much use of our field-putting machine which is also rigid and stable. The putter swings like a pendulum. Its speed is determined by how far back it is pulled prior to release. Important errors result if the release trigger mechanism is not carefully designed and if the structure can vibrate or move when it is triggered. Later chapters give more details on results beyond those described here. The field-putting machine tests provided essential inputs for our model such as scatter of stop points caused by the green itself.

The computer model makes it easy to compare the importance of errors. For example, consider putts where the golfer has an error, dAA, and keeps the putter square to the path rather than square to the

target. This causes lateral errors. If he then corrects only the putter orientation so that it stays square to the target, the error is only about 1/6th as large.

This is independent of the putt distance and does not depend on the golfer skill. Also, it is nearly independent of the putter design. Thus, it is about 6 times as important to orient the face correctly as compared to correctly orienting the direction of the swing path. Most serious golfers realize that it is more important to orient the face correctly, but aren't sure of the relative importance.

RESULTS

Our tests on greens show that loft angle of the putter between about zero and 6 degrees has little effect on variations of the stop point (scatter), provided the putter head speed is adjusted slightly to suit the loft angle. Negative loft angles and positive loft angles greater than about 6 degrees increase the scatter significantly.

Our model showed that the up-down location of the center of gravity of the head should be reasonably near the same height as the center of a golfer's hit pattern. The reasons for this will be explained in Chapter 33.

From the model we found that side spin of the ball after impact has a negligible effect on the path of the ball. Experiments show that if you align strongly to the left of the target, say about 30 degrees, and square the face about 5 degrees to the right of the target, the ball can be made to travel toward the target. The ball has considerable side spin, but the path of the ball is so near to straight that its slight curvature is not easy to see.

It is important to notice that putting and short chip shots are different with respect to how to best orient the face, compared to aiming when using other clubs, as discussed in Chapter 25. The putter face should be square to the target direction; for the other clubs, the club face should be square to the clubhead path direction. The reason is that with short shots, speed of the ball through the air is low so that there is negligible aerodynamic effect and thus no hook or slice problem during flight.

Our computer model allows us to calculate the effects of face surface shapes on the scatter of stop points of putts which result from the scatter of a golfer's hit points on the face. With this procedure, we studied curvature of the putter face and found that slight curvature may improve accuracy, but only to a negligible extent. If the radius of curvature of the face surface is as small as for some putters presently being advertised, small, undesirable, and unnecessary distance errors are introduced.

The model also makes it practical to define a performance rating so that accuracy of various putters can be compared quantitatively. Chapter 36 will describe this.

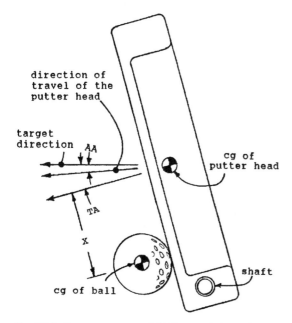

Fig. 27-1 *Our computer model of impact is based on this physical model. Only a few of the numerous variables are shown. A golfer normally tries to minimize the variables AA, TA, and x. We measure his failure to do so by their respective standard deviations dAA, dTA, and dLA.*

TECHNICAL NOTES

Our sub-model for travel of the ball after impact is defined by the equations below for flight distance, sliding distance, roll distance, and total distance for a putt, with the definitions which are given. We found the equation for the friction coefficient (Cb) from experimental measurements by dragging balls on greens.

This sub-model is for cases where side spin is reasonably small. Reference 16 gives further refinement for a ball with side spin and allows the resulting slight lateral variations to be calculated. That refinement could be included for cases where it might seem important, but for our uses, it is a negligible effect.

AE = elevation angle of launched ball [rad]
$\quad$ AV = initial angular velocity of ball [rad/sec]
$\quad$ (negative for backspin)
DF = horizontal flight distance [ft]
DR = distance of rolling [ft]
DS = distance of sliding [ft]
PD = total distance of putt [ft]
Cb = friction coefficient for ball sliding on grass []
g $\;$ = acceleration of gravity [ft/sec^2]
Mb = moment of inertia of ball [slug-ft^2]
Rb = radius of ball [ft]
S $\;\;$ = Stimp reading of green [ft]
TS $\;$ = time of sliding [sec]
VL $\;$ = launch velocity of ball [ft/sec]
VR $\;$ = velocity of ball when sliding stops [ft/sec]
Wb = weight of ball [lb]

(1) Cb = .946 − .021 ∗ S for Stimp of 4 or greater []
(2) DF = 2 ∗ VL^2 ∗ cosAE ∗ sinAE/g [ft]
(3) TS = (VL ∗ cosAE − AV ∗ Rb)/(Cb(g + Wb ∗ Rb^2/MB)) [sec]
(4) VR = VL ∗ cosAE − g ∗ Cb ∗ TS [ft/sec]
(5) DS = (VL ∗ cosA − g ∗ Cb ∗ TS/2) ∗ TS [ft]
(6) DR = .0477 ∗ S ∗ VR^1.595 [ft]
(7) PD = DF + DS + DR [ft]

HIT PATTERN ERRORS IN PUTTING

Would you believe that off-center putts are not as disastrous as they sound? Different strokes for different blokes. After reading this chapter, you'll be prepared for Chapter 29 and lower scores.

We measured errors made by golfers for use with our model to optimize putter designs. Of particular interest was the measurement of scatter of hits by golfers on the face of the putter, because these are errors, effects of which an optimized design can reduce. Information has not been published on scatter of hits on the face so, as with woods and irons, we made these specific measurements with a number of golfers.

The measurements and the model showed that hit pattern errors have a surprisingly small effect on most putts. This will surprise many golfers, mainly because off-center hits cause much more scatter for other clubs. This chapter describes these errors and later chapters will discuss how they affect the stop points of putts, along with other errors and their effects.

Figure 28-1 shows the nature of the scatter of hits on the face of a putter for a typical golfer. We made these measurements by applying marking tape to the face of the club and by measuring locations of the centers of the imprints after each putt. We measured these patterns for 50 hits by each of 17 golfers of various handicaps.

Figure 28-1 shows the scatter (the hit pattern) of an individual golfer's hits from the center (or average) location of his hits. The location of the centers of the hit pattern for various golfers may also vary (not shown in the figure). We are concerned both with scatter shown by the hit pattern and with the scatter of centers of hit patterns for many golfers. The elliptical shape shown indicates the general nature of the scatter of the hits and is explained further in the Technical Notes.

Figure 28-2 shows how the size of this hit pattern varies with HCP. The figure caption explains how this pattern can be interpreted to indicate sizes of ellipses which contain other percentages of hits.

To emphasize: Figure 28-2 gives the scatter of hits for each golfer from the center of his own hit pattern. When all golfers are considered, we found that the centers of hit patterns are not at the putter face center but are also scattered over the putter face.

Some golfers group their hit patterns high, some low, some toward the toe and some toward the heel. Figure 28-3 shows how the centers of hit patterns scatter over the face for the entire group of golfers tested. Surprisingly, unlike the results in Figure 28-2, the scatter of these centers did not depend significantly on a golfer's HCP.

Both Figures 28-2 and 28-3 show that some golfers center their hits so high on the face that the bottom of the putter is scuffing into the grass. In the figures, "scuff" refers to the bottom of the putter sweeping down into the grass.

Some scuffs may be rather deep and therefore cause significant drag with resulting distance error. For high HCP golfers, some may reach the soil causing large distance loss for the putt.

Slight scuffs are, by far, the most common and cause only negligible distance errors, particularly for long putts. Our extensive research on scuffing has

SYMBOLS AND DEFINITIONS	
AA alignment angle.*	the pattern and is approximately in the up-down direction.
dAA [deg] standard deviation of AA.	
dHS [%] standard deviation of HS just before impact as a percent of HS.	**dTA** [deg] standard deviation of TA.
	HCP [ ] handicap.
dLA [in] standard deviation of the centers of imprint locations on the club face, measured in the direction of the long axis of the pattern of these imprints. dLA extends approximately in the toe-heel direction.	**HS** [mph] head speed.*
	TA [deg] target angle for putters as defined in Figure 27-1.
	target direction [deg] also called launch direction. It is the direction in which you want to launch the ball.
dSA [in] same as dLA but measured in the direction of the short axis of	* More detail will be found for these items in the Appendix.

shown that it can be somewhat important for golfers with high HCP, particularly when they center their hit patterns rather high (which means the sole of the putter is rather low). Scuffing is discussed in detail in Chapter 35.

For use in the computer model, we express the hit patterns discussed above in equations given in the Technical Notes.

Variation arises in the angular position of the club face just before impact if the wrists are rotated from their normal and intended position. TA is what we call this angular position and dTA (the standard deviation) is what we call its variations.

Most golfers try to avoid wrist rotation during a putt and this helps minimize dTA. Unlike when analyzing the other clubs, for putters we include the effects of variations of wrist angle as part of the values of dAA and dTA.

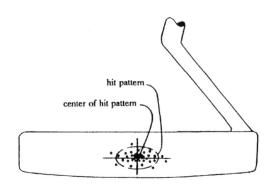

Fig. 28-1 *A golfer's scatter of points on a putter at the centers of impacts with the ball, called the "hit pattern". The center of the pattern of hits is also shown. It may or may not be at the center of the putter face.*

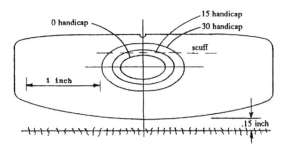

Fig. 28-2 *Effect of handicap on size of hit patterns. These ellipses contain 98.9% of all hits. Patterns 2/3rds of these sizes contain 86.5% of hits and 1/3rd these sizes contain 39.3% of hits. These are deviations of hits from the center of the hit pattern for each golfer. (See Figure 28-3).*

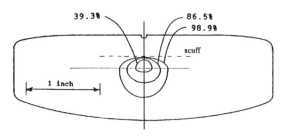

Fig. 28-3 *These curves show the scatter of the centers of hit patterns for various golfers. The percentages indicated show the portion of centers which are inside of each curve. The curves do not depend significantly on handicap. It shows that golfers often do not center their hits on the center of the face.*

TECHNICAL NOTES

In statistical terms, for each individual golfer, the hits were found to be normally distributed. For ellipse length in the toe-heel direction, we found that the 6-sigma fraction (which is 3-sigma each way, to include 99.7%) of hits can be expressed mathematically:

length of long axis $= 6*dLA = .606 + .0174*HCP$ [in].

A similar equation for up-down hits is:

length of short axis $= 6*dSA = .312 + .0101*HCP$ [in].

Accordingly for HCP of 0, 15, and 30, respective widths of the ellipse are .606, .868, and 1.129 inches. Respective heights are .312, .463, and .614. These 3-sigma ellipses include 98.9% of the hits because both errors are present (the "joint probability"), whereas the above 99.7% figure applies when only one or the other error is considered.

In the toe-heel direction the mean location of the centers of the hit patterns of the various golfers was .054 inch toward the toe, a negligible amount. These centers were normally distributed with 3-sigma value of .325 inch. We modeled the up-down centers of the hit patterns as a gamma distribution and found 99.7% were within a band .51 inch high. Neither correlated significantly with handicap.

The mean vertical distance from the bottom of the putter down to the bottom of the ball was .15 inch, independent of HCP.

HEAD SPEED, ALIGNMENT, THE GREEN, AND OTHER PUTTING ERRORS

YOU, OF COURSE, KNOW THAT YOU'LL NOT SINK A PUTT UNLESS YOU SQUARE THE FACE TO THE TARGET LINE. READ ON. YOU'LL ABSORB USEFUL DATA ON THIS AND OTHER FLAWS.

Golfer errors are variations from intended values of the swing and impact, such as variations of HS, AA, and off-center hits. Golfer errors which cause the most important errors in stop points (when the ball stops where you do not want it to stop) are represented as standard deviations dTA, dHS, and dAA.

Notice that dHS is expressed as percentage variation of HS, unlike the other 2 errors, which are measured in degrees.

The computer model shows that if the face is kept square to the target (TA = 0), errors in stop point due to dAA are only about 1/6th as large as when the face is kept square to the path of the putter head. Other authors have reported a similar relation. Other errors of stop point remain and the most important are dHS and imperfections of greens.

In Chapter 28 we discussed the scatter of hits over the putter face. They cause much smaller stop point errors, which are normally negligible compared with other errors. Though small, they are minimized by optimizing the weight (mass) distribution, cg location, and LA. Design improvements do little or nothing to reduce stop point errors caused by input errors other than the scatter of hits on the face, and do very little for the latter.

Scuffing the putter sole into the grass is often important for golfers with high HCP. Less important

errors are the press angle, (which means that the hands may be somewhat forward or aft of the putter head at impact), whether or not the golfer's eyes are over the ball, and others which are still smaller. It is useful for serious golfers to be aware of these errors and their effects.

HEAD SPEED ERRORS

We measured stop point errors for golfers of various abilities, making putts on flat greens. These measurements gave the standard deviations of the distance errors for each golfer. The computer model allowed calculation of the corresponding dHS. We found that dHS depends rather strongly on HCP and it can be described in a simple equation as given in the Technical Notes. It does not, however, depend significantly on the length of the putt or on green speed.

Our values for dHS for putters are about the same as for drivers.

ERRORS IN ALIGNMENT ANGLE AND SQUARING THE FACE TO THE TARGET

We found dTA and dAA from the same measurements of scatter of stop points described above for dHS. In this case, more experimental measurements of dTA and dAA would be desirable. See more details in the Technical Notes.

IRREGULARITIES OF THE GREEN

We used our field putting machine for testing of the effects of green irregularities which cause variations of the stop point. The machine can launch putts with near perfect repeatability. It can move the path aside in small steps for each new trial so that each putt has a new path but with no variation of direction. This feature is significant because repeated test putts on exactly the same path use only one part of the green

SYMBOLS AND DEFINITIONS		
AA alignment angle.*	**dTA**	[deg] standard deviation of TA.
dAA [deg] standard deviation of AA.	**HCP**	[ ] handicap.
dGA [deg] angular errors in putting due solely to imperfections of the green.	**HS**	[mph] head speed.*
	TA	[deg] target angle for putters as defined in Figure 27-1.*
dGR [ft] distance errors in putting due solely to imperfections of the green.	**target direction**	[deg] also called launch direction. It is the direction in which you want to launch the ball.
dHS [%] the standard deviation of HS just before impact as a percent of HS.	* *More detail will be found for these items in the Appendix.*	

and thus, are a poor test of the green's average condition. Much more important reasons to use a new path for each putt are that the first putt doesn't go as far as later putts on the same path and later putts have smaller lateral deviations as if there was a slight groove caused by the first putt.

On a good green these tests showed that standard deviation of stop points, both for distance and lateral errors, was 2% of the putt distance. For example, standard deviation errors caused solely by the green for a 10 foot putt would be 2.4 inches, (2% of 120 inches) both for distance and lateral errors. Surprisingly, both distance and lateral variations are about the same. More detail is in the Technical Notes.

These errors caused by greens are important errors, but are less important than dTA, dAA, and dHS. Our calculations show that greens with no such errors would allow golfers with HCP zero to reduce variations of their stop points about 22% for lateral errors and about 9% for distance errors. For HCP 30, the corresponding results are 17% and 2%.

OTHER ERRORS

Some golfers position their hands farther forward at impact than usual (the press angle). It causes an effect approximately the same as if the putter had lower loft angle and is not detrimental.

We have not measured press angle variations on actual golfers, but calculations of the effect with our computer model show that any effect will probably be close to negligible. For a well-designed putter on flat greens at Stimp 10, we find that variations of press angle as much as plus or minus 3 degrees cause distance errors for 5 foot putts of about .7 inch, and for 15 foot putts, about .9 inch. Thus press angle errors cause small distance errors and insignificant lateral errors.

When a golfer swings the putter too low, the imprint is high on the face and he scuffs into the grass. For high HCP golfers, scuffing can be important. This is discussed in Chapter 35.

There are also design errors which usually cause near-negligible errors in the stop point of putts. Often, moments of inertia are unnecessarily small. Stop point errors caused by hit pattern errors are greater if the cg is seriously mislocated. Some putter faces are cast and may not be flat. Our measurements of such putters show undesirable small errors in

direction of the putt, but we believe nearly all modern faces are sufficiently flat to avoid such errors. Putters with soft faces are popular. They reduce a small effect due to the dimples on the ball. We have found that a hit which is centered on the edge of a dimple has a small lateral error as compared with hitting between dimples.

Table 29-1 shows the rather large stop point errors caused by all of the input errors in combination, except scuffing. Scuffing is usually a minor error as further discussed in Chapter 35.

Table 29-1 *Stop point errors when all golfer errors are present except scuffing. These are the standard deviations, where dR is the distance and dA is the lateral spread [deg] measured at the aim point. They depend little on Stimp.*

putt distance, ft	HCP	HS, mph	dR, ft	dA, deg
5	0	2.07	.27	1.7
5	15	2.07	.40	1.8
5	30	2.07	.52	1.8
10	0	3.13	.54	1.7
10	15	3.13	.79	1.8
10	30	3.13	1.05	1.8
40	0	7.12	2.14	1.7
40	15	7.12	3.17	1.8
40	30	7.12	4.20	1.8

TECHNICAL NOTES

Irregularities of the green cause this standard deviation in the radial distance:

dGR = .020 ∗ PD [ft] where PD is putt distance [ft].

and greens cause this standard deviation in direction:

dGA = 1.15 [deg].

These are results found by measurements with our field putting machine at Stimp 8. We believe they do not depend strongly on Stimp, and that expressed this way, dGA does not depend on distance.

The green irregularities happen to cause the same lateral distance scatter as radial distance scatter. This seems surprising and we have no explanation. Further testing of the effects of green irregularities would be desirable.

Golfer standard deviation in HS for putting is:

dHS = 2.97 + .106 ∗ HCP [% of HS].

It is interesting that this dHS is nearly the same as for other clubs as given in Chapter 4.

Standard deviation of golfer errors in dAA and in squaring the putter face to the target (dTA) are:

dAA = 2 ∗ dTA [deg], and

dTA = 1.50 + .006 ∗ HCP [deg].

Our values for dAA and dTA are partly estimates. We found them by determining the values necessary when combined with our measured values of green errors to explain the lateral standard deviations of stop points which are given in Table 29-1. This was done by iterations with our model. It was necessary to estimate the ratio of dAA to dTA in order to get a unique solution. We chose 2 for the ratio, partly based on a few earlier measurements of putting errors. Putter performance and other uses of dTA and dAA in the book depend little on this ratio. More measurements of dTA and dAA would be desirable. Direct measurements are practical by such techniques as high speed movies or by strobe photos in subdued light.

EFFECTIVE HOLE DIAMETER AND THE HOLE ZONE

WOULD YOU BE SURPRISED TO KNOW THAT AN ELEMENT OTHER THAN YOUR VISION MAY MAKE THE CUP LOOK LARGER? FIND OUT ABOUT THIS AND THE "HOLE ZONE."

When a ball is centered on the hole as it approaches, it will drop in if it just reaches the edge of the hole. It will also drop in if it has enough excess speed to travel several feet past the hole if the hole was covered. However, if its excess speed is too great it will not drop.

When the ball is not centered on the hole, the excess speed must be less if it is to drop into the hole. Near the left or right edge, the excess speed must be small. This excess speed governs the distance past the hole at which the ball would stop if the hole was covered. We call the locations of the maximum distance where the ball could stop for successful putts "the hole zone." We measured the hole zone as described in the next section.

Thus, by definition, putts which stop inside this hole zone when the hole is covered would drop when the hole is open. The hole zone concept is important to help golfers judge how far to aim, and it is essential to our analysis of putting success, as will be seen here and in succeeding chapters. Most of Chapters 28, 29, 30, 31, and 32 were published in Reference 14.

OUR TESTS ON ACTUAL GREENS

To define the hole zone, we needed to know how much error in putt distance and how much lateral error could be tolerated before the putt fails to drop. To find out, we rolled many balls down a ramp which controlled ball speed by how far up the ramp we released the ball. This test was done on flat, level greens, taking care to use several directions to avoid the effect of grain or slight slope.

With the ramp just a few inches from the edge of the hole, we aimed at the center of the hole and increased speed until the ball was going too fast to drop.

Next, we aimed slightly to the side and repeated the steps, continuing the process, aiming more and more to the side of the hole until the ball reached the edge of the cup.

We made similar tests with the ramp, but with no hole, to study how distance of the roll depends on the initial velocity of the ball. From this test, we developed an empirical equation for the roll distance, DR, discussed in Chapter 27 and more fully in the Technical Notes below.

The equation for the roll distance, DR, then allowed us to convert the measurements of speed, when the hole was present, into the distance each ball would have rolled if the hole had been smoothly covered. This defined the hole zone and its usefulness for golfers is discussed below.

THE EFFECTIVE HOLE DIAMETER

As a byproduct of this work, we found that the effective diameter of the hole is larger when the Stimp reading is low. An equation which represents this effect is given in the Technical Notes. Table 30-1 shows the effective diameter of the cup at various Stimp readings and the amount of increase over the basic cup diameter, based on this equation.

When the grass is deep and slow and the ball is rolling very slowly near the edge of the cup, there are fewer blades of grass supporting the ball on the side nearest the hole, so it tends to move toward the hole. When the green is fast, the ball sinks less deep into the grass and this effect is reduced. This data is for bent grass. Bermuda grass may be somewhat different. This increase in the effective diameter is a factor which makes putting a little easier for slow greens than would be the case on fast greens.

THE HOLE ZONE

The left side of Figure 30-1 shows the results of the distance measurements and the small effect of the varying effective diameter of the hole. This is the "hole zone." The Stimp reading has a large effect, and we found that the length of the hole zone was proportional to Stimp. It surprised us that at Stimp 9, successful putts aimed directly at the center of the hole could travel up to 58.2 inches beyond the hole if the hole was absent. This distance diminishes very rapidly when such putts are slightly off center. This is shown by the rather sharp tip of the hole zone at the top of Figure 30-1.

The right side of the figure shows that putts which are shorter than about 10 feet have broader hole zones than the longer putts. To understand why the hole zone gets broader, assume your putt distance was extremely short, say, half the hole diameter from the edge of the cup. In this case, you could aim very far to the right or left and the ball would (likely) still drop. A calculation shows that for the correct ball velocity, you could aim 30 degrees, either right or left. Now if the hole was covered, the putts would travel well to the right or left, making a very broad hole zone.

Figure 30-2 shows how uphill, downhill, and sidehill putts affect the hole zone and is only intended to show trends in each situation. We did no research to experimentally evaluate the hole zone for sloping greens.

The hole zone is an interesting concept, but its real value is that it provides an essential part of the information we need in order to calculate items of direct interest and utility.

One is the optimum distance past the hole at which a golfer should plan for the ball to stop if the hole were absent, described in Chapter 32. The hole zone facilitates calculation of one putter design's performance compared with another.

It also allows ranking the importance of the golfer errors on success of putts, thus showing a golfer which error is most important to try to reduce.

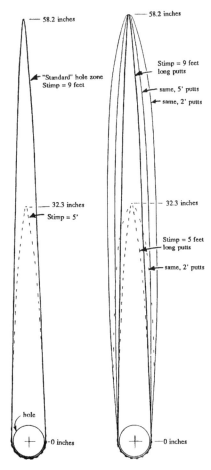

Fig. 30-1 *The "Hole Zone". Refer to the left drawing. Putts which would stop inside these envelopes if the hole were covered, would drop when the hole is present. Those stopping outside would not drop. This is for flat, level greens. Hole zone length is proportional to Stimp reading. Curves for Stimp 9 and 5 show this effect. The right drawing shows that when the putt distance is shorter than about 10 feet, the hole zone becomes wider as the outer contours indicate. The curves show that putts can go 58.2 inches past the hole for Stimp 9, if they are on the center of the hole, but much less if even slightly off center.*

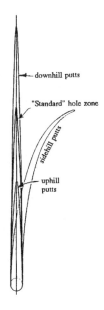

← downhill putts

"Standard" hole zone

sidehill putts

← uphill
putts

Fig. 30-2 *This drawing shows how the hole zone is effectively much longer for downhill putts and shorter for uphill putts, as would be expected. Sidehill putts curve the hole zone to the side. These are not based on analysis as in the case of flat greens and are only intended to show the trends.*

Table 30-1 *Effective hole diameter is larger for slow greens.*

Stimp feet	diameter inches	increase inches
∞	4.25	.0
15	4.51	.26
12	4.57	.32
9	4.68	.43
6	4.89	.64

TECHNICAL NOTES

The following are empirical equations which approximate our experimental measurements. The distance equation from Chapter 27, for roll of the ball on a level green without slip is:

$$DR = .0477 * S * VR^{1.595} \text{ [ft]}$$

where DR means roll distance in feet, S is Stimp reading in feet, and VR is ball velocity in feet/sec at start of the roll.

Notice that this does not include the early parts of a putt, of which 1% to 3% of the total putt distance is flight distance and about 10% to 30% is motion for which the ball is partly sliding and partly rolling (which will be described in Chapter 31).

The above equation for DR could be somewhat improved if a different functional form had been used. For the ball to stop on a slope, the drag force must have a non-zero value as the ball's velocity approaches zero. On a typical green, a ball will stop rolling if the slope is less than about 3 degrees, but continue if it is a little higher. This angle must depend on Stimp, though we did not investigate this.

For our research, the above equation gives reasonable accuracy for the roll distance, but not the detail of getting there. We used this 3-degree angle in our study of lateral motion of putts with slope near the golfer and near the hole, which will be discussed in Chapter 34.

The equation for effective hole radius (Rh) in inches with S in feet is:

$$Rh = 2.125 + 1.944/S \text{ [in]}.$$

For putts longer than about 10 feet, the following equations describe the hole zone in 2 parts. Zs is the Z coordinate of the hole zone short of the hole center and Zb is the coordinate beyond the hole center, both in inches. S is the Stimp value in feet, X is the magnitude of the distance in the X direction (lateral direction) in inches, $X <= Rh$, and Xh is X/Rh.

$$Zs = -Rh * SQR(1 - Xh^2) \text{ [in]} \text{ and}$$

$$Zb = S * (6.154 * (1 - Xh^2) + .309e^{(-50 * Xh^2)}) \text{ [in]}.$$

The first equation describes the hole zone short of the hole center as a semicircle. The 2nd equation describes the hole zone beyond the hole center as a parabolic shape with a small sharpening at the tip caused by the exponential term.

Both allow for the change of hole zone length and hole diameter with Stimp. For putts shorter than 10 feet, the hole zone becomes wider beyond the hole center and this feature is not described by these equations. We used a more complex function using polar coordinates to model the wider hole zone for short putts

In our measurements of the actual hole zone, using a ball rolling down a ramp, it is important that the test ramp must cause the appropriate rate of spin on the ball as it rolls down. For example, consider a ramp made of 2 parallel bars. If the bars are slender and 1.5 inch apart where they contact the ball, the spin rate of the ball will be 122% greater than the rate for rolling on a flat ramp. If 1 inch apart, this is 22% greater; for .5 inch apart, 5% greater; and .25 inch apart, 1% greater.

We used a very open V-shaped trough. Its side-to-side angle was 172 degrees which is equivalent to .25 inch bar spacing.

Our experimental evaluation of the length of the hole zone was made on a practice green for which the hole was rather newly cut and little used. Thus, the edge of the hole may have been a little sharper than an average hole.

Reference 9 reports a "doughnut" effect near the hole where the grass has been altered slightly by frequent trampling by golfers within a foot or 2 of the hole. More experimental evaluation of these characteristics would be desirable to quantize their influence on the effective diameter of the hole, length of the zone, and scatter caused by the grass. We believe this would have only a small effect on our results.

TRAVEL OF THE BALL AND THE STOP ZONE

I T IS NO SECRET THAT A PUTT ROLLS, BUT WHAT HAPPENS WHEN THE BALL FLIES OR SLIDES? WE'RE CERTAIN YOU HAVE A GOOD MENTAL PICTURE OF THE "SCATTER OF STOP POINTS". CHECK OUT OUR CALCULATIONS OF SUCCESSFUL PUTTS. THEY WILL PROVIDE INTERESTING AND HELPFUL INSIGHTS.

In a putt, how far does a ball fly, how far does it slide, and how far does it roll? This chapter discusses the answers by use of the model and the "stop zone," the scatter of points where the ball stops.

You probably have a mental picture of how much the stop points of your unsuccessful putts deviate from the hole. In this chapter, we will explain this subject in great detail.

Chapter 30 explained the hole zone, the area on the putting green where balls would stop for *successful* putts if the hole was covered. When *unsuccessful* putts are also included, the scatter of stop points is what we call the stop zone. The stop zone is generally much larger and of different shape, compared to the hole zone. When we know the hole zone and the stop zone, then we are able to calculate which fraction would actually stop in the hole zone. The remainder are unsuccessful putts.

This chapter will illustrate the stop zone's shape and size and explain how we studied it by experiments. Chapter 32 describes some very useful results of this research.

TRAVEL OF THE BALL ON A PUTT

Figure 31-1 shows that for Stimp above 8 and putts over about 10 feet, flight of the ball is about 2 to 4% of the total putt distance and the sliding and rolling part is roughly 10%. The remainder is simple roll without sliding. This is for a well-designed putter with 3 degrees loft.

The ball leaves the putter head in a small upward angle (unless the loft angle is zero or negative) and with a small amount of backspin. Thus it flies a very short distance and maintains its backspin. When it reaches the ground, there is negligible bounce, but it must slide until its backspin is gone and it has picked up enough forward spin so that sliding stops and the motion becomes simple rolling. That phrase is often called skidding. From there to the hole, it continues as simple rolling. Equations for this motion are in Chapter 27.

Although putters with more loft have somewhat more flight and with less loft they have less flight, in all cases, flight is never more than a few percent of the total putt distance. Green speed (Stimp) affects slide and roll distances as Figure 31-1 shows.

MEASUREMENTS OF THE STOP ZONE

A number of golfers with a variety of handicaps helped us to get data on the stop zone. Each golfer made many putts toward a target spot 12 feet away but with no hole and on a level green with Stimp 7.5 feet. For each putt, the radial distance from the golfer to the stop point and its lateral distance from the aim line were measured. The Technical Notes explain how we reduced this data and found the dependence on HCP and distance.

The results scaled for a 10 foot putt are shown in Figure 31-2. Remember that each of these curves contain 98.9% of measured putts for the indicated HCP, and that they include all putting errors for level greens except serious scuffing. The figure caption explains how to visualize smaller curves which would contain 86.5% and 39.3% of points.

Figure 31-3 shows how these curves change for other putt distances. Notice that the scale for Figure 31-3 is very different from Figure 31-2. A distance scale is marked on each to facilitate comparison.

Figure 31-3 also contains black areas which are the hole zones, drawn to scale. All putts which stop in the black area represent successful putts which would have dropped if the hole were not covered. Very few putts drop for the 40-foot putt distance, while the 10-foot putts are much better. Most 5-foot putts drop, especially for the lower HCP curves. Of course, this is as expected: more putts will fall for better golfers, and a 5 or 10-foot putt is easier to make than a much longer one.

In judging the curves, especially for the 5-foot putts, remember that the central parts of the zone have the highest density of stop points and that the outer margins near each curve boundary have much less dense concentration of stop points.

Low HCP golfers have another important advantage when greens are not level – their skill at reading such greens. We did not test this effect.

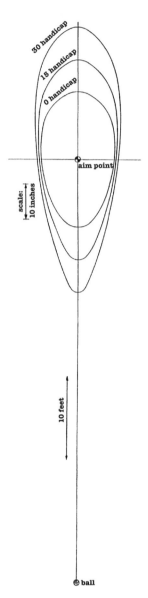

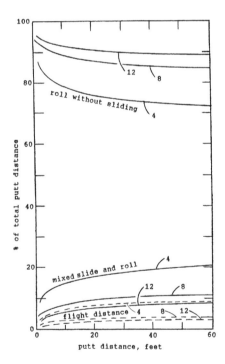

Fig. 31-1 *Details of the ball travel after impact on a level green. Numbers on the curves are green speed (Stimp). The 3 lower curves with dashed lines are for flight distance.*

Fig. 31-2 *The "stop zone." Putts intended to stop at a point 10 feet away on a level green will scatter as shown. These curves contain 98.9% of points. Curves 2/3rds the length and width contain 86.5% of points and 1/3rd as large contain 39.3% and are of more elliptical shape. Stimp has little effect.*

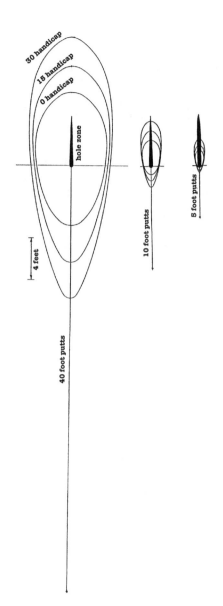

Fig. 31-3 *Stop zones for various putt distances and handicaps, with distance beyond the hole adjusted for each handicap so as to minimize the number of putts to hole out. The black shape is the hole zone for Stimp 7.5 as explained in Chapter 30. These curves are smaller scale versions of Figure 31-2 except the center of each curve has been moved toward or away from the golfer so as to achieve minimum putts.*

TECHNICAL NOTES

All the usual errors of putting were present for data presented in Figure 31-2 except for serious scuffing. Data points for serious scuffs were omitted.

In approximate order of importance, these errors include those of head speed, aiming, disturbances from irregularities of the green, minor scuffing, toe-heel and up-down off-center hits, press angle (such as hands unusually forward or rearward at impact), eye position, and many smaller errors.

Golfer variations in confidence probably have a strong effect on these errors, although it was not measured. Some of these errors were discussed in recent chapters and future chapters will discuss others.

The results shown apply only to level, well-maintained greens. Sloping greens tend to give considerably larger scatter of stop points.

Examination of the data on individual golfers showed that both distance and lateral scatter were reasonably close to statistical normal distributions.

The distance scatter was nearly proportional to the intended distance, as expected. With this approximation, we found a least-squares linear fit to all of the data. This gave the results in the form of these equations for the standard deviations:

$$dR = (12*Ph+AD)*(.644+.0205*HCP) \text{ [in] and}$$

$$dA = 1.718+.0039*HCP \text{ [deg]},$$

where dR is the standard deviation for radial distance variations (1-sigma) in inches, dA is the standard deviation of angular errors (direction errors) in degrees, HCP is handicap, AD is aim distance beyond the hole (see Chapter 32), and Ph is the distance to the center of the hole in feet.

These equations conform to Figures 31-2 and 31-3 when multiplied by 3 to give 3-sigma values which extend each direction from the aim point in the figures. (Note: they also apply to Table 29-1.)

The angular width of the hole zone, given by the equation for dA, shows only a small dependence on HCP. This width depends strongly on how well a golfer can properly orient the club face (choose the proper TA) when aiming his putt. The width depends relatively little on AA if TA is correct as discussed in Chapter 29.

The perception of proper TA depends on some characteristic of vision which we think does not change much with practice or golfer skill, unlike making the proper swing direction, having the right head speed, reading the green, etc. This may explain why the width of the stop zone does not depend strongly on a golfer's HCP.

PUTTER AIMING AND THE AIM DISTANCE

IT IS OBVIOUS THAT IF YOU'RE ON THE GREEN IN TWO AND YOUR BIRDIE PUTT HANGS ON THE LIP, YOU CAN'T PUT A SCORE OF THREE ON YOUR CARD. LEARN HOW YOU CAN MAKE THE MOST OF YOUR SKILLS. SEEING THE BALL DISAPPEAR IS AN UPLIFTING EXPERIENCE.

Most golfers know they should try to hit putts hard enough to travel somewhat beyond the center of the hole. Exactly how far beyond is based on reasonably good estimates by good golfers. Studies by others have concluded that many golfers tend to putt too short.

In this chapter, our research results give definite information about how far you should aim past the center of the hole. We call this the "aim distance," AD; "aim point" is the ideal aiming point at the AD beyond the center of the hole.

Chapter 31 explained the stop zone which is the pattern of points around the target where putts will stop. Chapter 30 explained the hole zone which is an area beyond the hole where successful putts would have stopped, had the hole been covered. When we properly study the stop zone together with the hole zone it is possible to find the optimum value for AD to finish putting with the fewest putts for level greens.

You should think about AD when setting up for a putt. Usually, golfers are told to aim 15 to 18 inches past the hole. This is helpful advice, but incomplete because it doesn't show how AD depends on HCP, Stimp, and on putt distance. This chapter will provide somewhat different and more accurate advice and will show that AD varies with putt distance, HCP, and S.

In rare cases, AD may even be negative for high HCP, low Stimp, and long putts. Negative AD means intended putt distance is short of the center of the hole. Although at first, this concept seems wrong, its reality is explained below.

As with the hole zone and the stop zone, this chapter's discussion relates to putts on level greens. Adjustments by golfers will be needed when the green is not level.

THE AIM POINT AND AIM DISTANCE

The Technical Notes explain how the computer model analyzed the hole zone together with the stop zone to find the optimum aim point for minimum strokes to hole out on level greens, regardless of the condition of the green. Figure 32-1 shows the result of these calculations.

It appears surprising that AD can be slightly negative for high HCP golfers. It is because some of their putts spread out laterally so much that if going very far beyond the hole, the distance for the next putt is somewhat more than if equally short of the hole. This is related to the fact that for long first putts, many second putts are not successful. At 40 feet, 3 inches short is only .6% of the putt distance and that distance is almost negligible.

Greens which are not level may alter AD considerably. Golfer skill is the only practical way to adjust AD to suit such cases. AD as discussed here is a useful basis for making such judgements. AD is small and less important for putt distance less than about 5 feet.

These aim point results are in reasonable agreement with the studies reported in References 3 and 11, though our aim points are a little shorter, and more detailed. In those references, dependence of AD on HCP, Stimp, and putt distance was not considered. Another difference is that Reference 3 maximized the

SYMBOLS AND DEFINITIONS		
AD [in] aim distance, the optimum distance beyond the center of the hole for aiming a putt.	**PD**	[ft] total distance of a putt.
	Ph	[ft] distance to center of hole for putting.
dR [in] standard deviation of putt distance with all errors present.	**PHO**	[ ] putts needed to hole out.
	S	[ft] Stimp reading.*
dX [in] standard deviation of lateral putt distance with all errors present.	**TA**	[deg] target angle for putters, as defined in Figure 27-1.
HCP handicap.		*More detail will be found for this item in the Appendix.

probability of success on a given putt, whereas we minimized the number of putts to hole out. That is, we gave consideration to the success of the remaining putts (if any) needed to hole out, as well as success on the first putt. This is a little different and more meaningful.

SOME USEFUL RULES

Figure 32-1 can be summarized with useful accuracy by a few reasonably simple rules. You may wish to memorize the statement below which best applies to your handicap. This is for Stimp 9.

For other Stimp ratings, uphill putts and downhill putts, and for putts shorter than 5 feet, refer to the suggested adjustments.

- *0 HCP golfers should use aim distances of 7 inches for 5-foot putts, increasing to 13 inches for 20-foot putts, diminishing to 7 inches for 40-foot putts.*

- *15 HCP golfers should use aim distances of 9 inches for 5-foot putts, increasing to 13 inches for 15-foot putts, diminishing to 3 inches for 40-foot putts.*

- *30 HCP golfers should use aim distances of 12 inches for 5 foot putts, increasing to 14 inches for 10 foot putts, diminishing to −3 inches (short) for 40 foot putts.*

Adjustments. For all putts longer than 5 feet, add about 2 inches for very fast greens and deduct about 2 inches for very slow greens. For putts shorter than 5 feet, diminish the 5 foot aim distances in proportion to the putt distance. Reduce aim distance for uphill putts and increase for downhill putts.

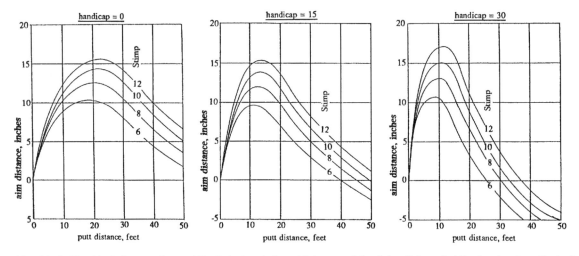

Fig. 32-1 *The ideal distance beyond the hole for aiming which we call the "aim distance", AD, showing the effect of Stimp. In a few cases, AD is negative (short of the hole). The curves are for flat, level greens.*

TECHNICAL NOTES

The calculation of aim distance (AD) uses a method that assumes all missed putts have a remaining hole distance (Ph) less than the original Ph. The method starts by considering a very short Ph for which the 3-sigma stop zone (other than 3-sigma could be used) is just contained in the hole zone for this Ph. For this and all shorter Ph values, putts to hole out (PHO) is 1.

Next, Ph is slightly increased beyond this first Ph for a second Ph. Using the procedure described in the following paragraph, the optimum AD and minimum PHO are determined by iterating on AD. The resulting AD and PHO are the desired values for the second Ph. The minimum PHO for the second Ph is needed to find AD for still longer Ph's. This step is repeated until the entire desired Ph range is covered.

For each step above, values are specified for Ph and AD. The stop zone for this PD is described by the density function for 2 orthogonal, normal, random variables, defined in Chapter 31 as:

$$dR = PD * (.644 + .0205 * HCP) \text{ [in]}$$
$$dX = PD * (.360 + .00082 * HCP) \text{ [in], where}$$
$$PD = Ph + AD/12,$$

where dR is the standard deviation for radial distance variations (1-sigma), HCP is handicap, and dX is the standard deviation of lateral distance variations.

PHO is found by numerical integration over the stop zone, the product: [probability of stopping in a rectangle with sides ΔZ by ΔX at point (Z,X)] times [remaining PHO] for this point. The first term is the product of the density function evaluated at (Z,X) times the area of the rectangle (ΔZ, ΔX).

The remaining PHO is zero if the point (Z,X) is in the hole zone and if not, it is the minimum PHO found earlier for the remaining hole distance associated with point (Z,X). PHO for the given Ph and AD is 1 plus the number of remaining putts.

SWEET SPOT, INERTIA, AND CENTER OF GRAVITY OF THE HEAD

HOW IMPORTANT IS LOCATION OF THE CENTER OF GRAVITY; THE INERTIA? WHY DOES THE COMPUTATION OF PAR INCLUDE TWO PUTTS PER GREEN? IF AFTER 18 HOLES, YOU HAVE USED LESS THAN 30 PUTTS, YOU ARE GOOD IF NOT, WELL WE CAN HELP YOU.

This chapter will illustrate the effects of moment of inertia and location of the cg of the head on the sweet spot and off-center hits, using representative putters. Chapter 36 will make a more complete and exact comparison among putters.

Golfer errors and other errors in a putt cause distance and lateral errors in the stop point; that is, input errors cause output errors. Mainly we are concerned with the relation between these input and output errors, and for input errors, off-center hits in particular.

THE EFFECTS OF OFF-CENTER HITS

Two putters are compared in Figures 33-1 and 33-2.

Putter A is the Tech Line Model 330, a putter designed for large moment of inertia around the vertical axis through the cg and optimum cg location. As a comparison, "Putter R" is a widely-respected design which has been popular with little change for many years. Many golfers think its general appearance is excellent. However, its cg is too high and it has smaller moments of inertia than most popular putters. Putter R was chosen for comparison because of its design characteristics, its reputation and frequency of use. The Technical Notes give additional detail about both putters.

Figure 33-1 shows the putter results for distance loss with two kinds of golfer errors, calculated using Stimp 9 greens. In all 4 of these graphs, notice that horizontal scales are much different from the vertical scales.

The lower 2 graphs show the distance errors caused by hits which are off center toward the heel or toe. The distance error caused by toe-heel errors is approximately proportional to the putt distance, for any given amount of off-center error.

The upper 2 graphs are for off-center hits which are upward or downward. There are small, medium, and large dots at the bottom of each graph. They show the ranges of hit pattern errors for 99.7% of hits for HCP 0, 15, and 30, respectively.

The two lower graphs in Figure 33-1 show that the toe-heel errors for Putter A cause much smaller distance errors than for Putter R. For example for Putter A with 15-foot putt distance, an off-center hit one inch toward the toe (–1 on the lower scale) causes the putt to be about 13 inches short as compared to a center hit (0 on the lower scale). For the same case with putter R, the distance loss is about 21 inches. These distance losses are nearly proportional to the putt distance for both graphs. In other words, Putter A is more forgiving of toe-heel errors.

These effects on the 2 lower graphs are almost entirely caused by differences in the moment of inertia about the vertical axis. The reason is that the putter head turns more for low inertia with off-center hits in the toe-heel direction, than for high inertia.

The 2 upper graphs in Figure 33-1 show the effect of Putter R's high cg. For putter R with 45-foot putts, if the ball is hit only about .2 inches upward or downward from the sweet spot, the top graphs show that the stop point distance may vary from about 5 inches too far to about 10 inches too short. The same error on Putter A causes loss of distance of only about 1 inch for each hit.

The best up-down location for the cg for putters is close the average height of the center of hit patterns as described in Chapter 28.

SYMBOLS AND DEFINITIONS	
cg [] center of gravity (more accurately, center of mass); its location is usually given in inches.	**putter A** an optimized design, our model 330.
HCP handicap.	**putter R** a popular design with low moments of inertia and cg which is much too high.

Figure 33-2 shows the corresponding lateral errors for toe-heel off-center hits for only one putt distance, namely 45 feet (an arbitrary putt distance for illustration.) These errors are nearly proportional to putt distance. For example a 4.5-foot putt has lateral errors only one-tenth as large as the 45-foot putts which are shown in Figure 33-2. Up-down errors cause negligible lateral errors when the cg is reasonably well located.

For putters, fore-aft position for the cg is best when in or reasonably near the face. A rearward position of the cg mainly affects lateral errors caused by toe-heel hitting errors, which are shown in Figure 33-2.

Putter R has its cg much closer to the face than Putter A. This is the principal reason why putter R has smaller errors shown in Figure 33-2. Large moment of inertia for Putter A does reduce this error, but the effect of its larger rearward cg distance predominates.

An optimum design requires a compromise among the cg location and moments of inertia, and it is necessary to depart from ideal fore-aft location of the cg in order to gain larger moments of inertia and thus optimum performance. Thus, even though Putter R causes smaller lateral errors (shown in Figure 33-2), they are small compared to the distance errors of Figure 33-1. In general, putts are more successful using Putter A as will be further discussed below and in the Technical Notes.

Tʜᴇ Sᴡᴇᴇᴛ Sᴘᴏᴛ

Golfers usually think of the "sweet spot" as the point on the club face for best putts and that's the meaning used here – one specific point on the club face and not a small area. A "large" sweet spot mainly means less effect for hits a small distance away from this point. Large moment of inertia about a vertical axis is the main cause of a large sweet spot.

Figures 33-1 and 33-2 also show that scatter of the stop points is negligible when hits are within about .3 inch of the face center, provided the up-down and toe-heel locations of the cg are also reasonably close to the face center, such as .2 inch. Study of the graphs shows that if hits are much farther from the center, such as .5 or .6 inch or more, the variations of stop points increase rapidly.

If the up-down and toe-heel cg location is farther

from the face center, you can still get accurate putts if you know where the cg is located and center your putts there.

Dɪꜱᴄᴜꜱꜱɪᴏɴ

For each putter head, these figures show the major effects of cg location and moment of inertia about a vertical axis. The toe-heel location of the cg and 5 other inertia terms cause smaller effects.

For ordinary off-center hits, these variations of stop points are much smaller than the variations caused by golfer errors in head speed and alignment.

For example, in the lower left part of Figure 33-1, the intermediate dots on the bottom line in the graph correspond to toe hits and heel hits for a 15 HCP golfer. Careful reading of the graph shows that they cause distance errors of less than 3 inches for 99.7% of 10-foot putts. The corresponding errors due to head speed variations as shown in Chapter 29 are 4.78 feet (57.4 inches).

When both the head speed error and the toe-heel error are present, the error is only 57.5 inches. The errors do not simply add together; instead the larger errors almost completely mask the smaller ones. The Technical Notes give more detail.

The result for putters, unlike drivers, is that differences among various models is largely masked by head speed and alignment errors. This is an important reason that putter R has been popular, even though its inertia is rather low and its cg is very high.

It may be concluded that cg location and inertia are of only modest importance for most putter designs.

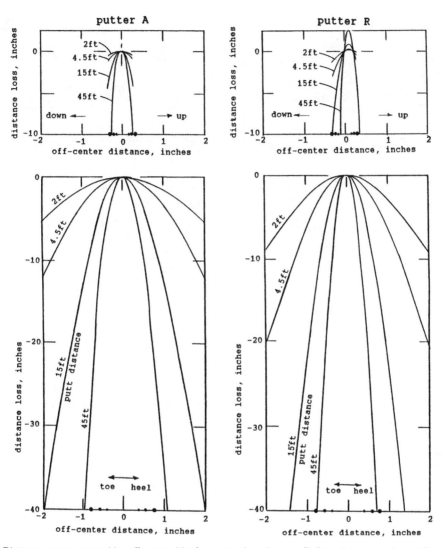

Fig. 33-1 *Distance errors caused by off-center hits for putter A and putter R. Putt distance in feet at Stimp 9 is marked on each curve. The lower graphs are for toe-heel errors and upper are for up-down errors. There are small, medium and large dots at the bottom of each graph, showing the ranges of hit pattern errors for 99.7% of hits for HCP 0, 15, and 30 respectively. Note: horizontal and vertical scales are different.*

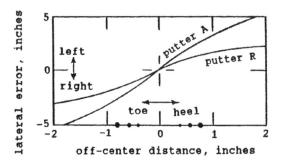

Fig. 33-2 *Lateral errors caused by toe-heel hits (see text regarding up-down hits). Both curves are for 45 foot putts at Stimp 9. The errors are proportional to putt distance. Note: horizontal and vertical scale factors are quite different. See the previous figure for meaning of dots at bottom of graph.*

TECHNICAL NOTES

For Putter A, in inches, the cg was .03 toward the heel from the face center, .00 above the center hit, and .59 behind a vertical plane tangent to the bottom of the face. For Putter R, the corresponding numbers were .13 toward the heel, .34 above the center hit and .15 behind the vertical plane.

The moment of inertia of the head about the vertical axis through the cg is the most important one for most purposes. For Putter A, it was 2.23 pound–in^2, or 1.74 times that of Putter R. Loft angle was 3 degrees for Putter A and about 4 for Putter R.

Regarding the combination of output errors, when independent errors are normal distributions and several errors are present, the resultant error is the square root of the sum of the squares of the individual errors (RSS).

This is why the example that combines toe-heel and head speed errors showed the error for the combination was only .1 inch larger than the larger of the two. The nature of the combination of errors explains why large errors mask small ones.

This is usually true even when the errors deviate considerably from normal distributions, but only when the errors are independent of each other. The effects of the combination can only be found by comparing outputs from the computer model, because the differences are so minor.

UNNECESSARY PUTTING ERRORS

SHOULD YOU USE PLUMB-BOBBING? IS SIDE SLOPE NEAR THE GOLFER MUCH MORE OR LESS IMPORTANT THAN MIDWAY OR NEAR THE HOLE? SHOULD YOU HIT OFF THE TOE ON SHORT DOWNHILL PUTTS? CLEAR YOUR MIND.

Some golfers make a few easily-avoided errors, which tend to be somewhat harmful to putting success. Our research is only concerned with errors that can be analyzed with reasonable accuracy from a technical viewpoint. Not examined are other golfer errors that can only be reduced or corrected by good instruction and practice.

This chapter relates to plumb-bobbing, effects of slope of the green, toe putts, cutting the ball, reading the grain of the grass, eyes over the ball, and keeping the putter face square during the swing.

PLUMB-BOBBING

Plumb-bobbing is common. Here is a clear description of what many golfers understand about plumb-bobbing, paraphrased from *GOLF*, May 1991 by Jonathan Abrahams, (used with permission of the publisher).

> With one eye open, stand with the ball, the cup, and your eye in line. Hold your putter lightly at the top of the grip. Move the putter left or right until the lower end of the shaft covers the ball. If the hole appears to the right of the shaft, the ground slopes left to right. If in line with the shaft, the ground is level. If to the left of the shaft, the ground slopes right to left.

There is a basic problem in the first sentence. The cup, the ball, and your eye are 3 points in space and they define a plane. This means they will appear to be in line to your eye, no matter where you position your eye and no matter what is the slope of the green. Although hard for many people to believe, this phenomenon is explained more fully in the Technical Notes.

For example, imagine that the ball is on a level part of the green, and the hole is not lower nor higher than the ball. Also, imagine that there is a large slope to the left or right near the hole. This does nothing to change the position of your eye. Also it would not change the position of the putter shaft nor the apparent location of the hole when you do the plumb-bobbing as stated. In this example, plumb-bobbing would tell you that there is no break in the putt even though the slope to the left or right near the hole definitely would cause a break.

Another example is the intermediate variation of slope. Imagine that both the ball and the hole are in level areas and at the same height. Also imagine an area between ball and hole, which slopes strongly to one side or the other. Plumb-bobbing would tell you there is no break, even though there is.

These examples show that plumb-bobbing would mislead you, and is thus more likely to increase errors, rather than reduce them. However, another use of plumb-bobbing can be helpful and that other use is discussed below.

Note also that a putter shaft hangs straight down as viewed by the golfer only if the cg of the club is located in line with the shaft axis in this view, which is rare in putters when viewed from the front or rear. This error is easily avoided by rotating the putter around a vertical axis until the shaft appears vertical from your point of view.

Checking relative to the vertical corner of a building will show you that either of 2 positions will do this, no matter where the cg is located. Either one is the position of interest.

A different and helpful use of plumb-bobbing is to use the putter only to judge if the green appears perpendicular to the shaft which means it is level. If it is not perpendicular, the vertical shaft helps you to estimate the slope of the green. This can be useful for judging the slope anywhere along the line of the putt and from various directions. Most useful may be to look along the line of the putt either toward the ball or toward the hole. Note that this usage does not involve the position of the ball or of the hole.

We suspect this is commonly done by some golfers. It is more accurate when the golfer bends low or squats to lower his eye level.

To summarize, golfers should not use plumb-bobbing to guide their putts in the manner of the paraphrased description because it will often increase their putting errors. For a different purpose, plumb-bobbing may be useful for judging the degree of slope of a green at points along the intended line of the putt.

WHERE THE SLOPE IS MOST IMPORTANT

Many golfers believe the slope near the hole is most important. There, the ball is moving slowly and has time to change direction much more than when it is far from the hole and moving faster.

However, far from the hole, where slope causes only a small change in direction, the small change in direction acts over a large distance.

Analysis shows that lateral errors caused by slope are 50 to 60% greater when the slope is near the hole as compared with when it is near the golfer. This result depends little on Stimp or putt distance.

Thus, you should not ignore side slope of the green near the ball, even though it is less important than slope near the hole.

TOE PUTTS

Some golfers believe that on downhill putts, it is helpful to hit far out on the toe of the putter to give the ball a lower velocity when it leaves the putter. A slower swing accomplishes the same effect.

In Chapter 33 we showed that an error in where you hit the ball is of little importance if it is a small distance to one side or the other of the ideal place to hit (the sweet spot). This is not true when the hit is a large distance from the sweet spot.

For hits far out to the toe or heel, a small change there makes a much larger distance error than a corresponding small change near the sweet spot. Trying to toe-putt accurately is simply an unnecessary additional error beyond your unavoidable normal errors.

It does not reduce the need to have the right

head speed. It also requires that you learn how fast to swing for a situation different from your normal putts.

CUTTING THE BALL

"Cutting the ball" in putting usually refers to a golfer making the head travel, not in the target direction, but strongly to one side, usually to their left for right-hand golfers. Then they open the club face strongly so it is square to the target direction. The result is that the ball travels approximately in the direction in which the face is aimed and the ball starts with much side spin.

Some believe that the side spin somehow helps the ball drop into the hole on short putts. The fact is that side spin is quickly eliminated by sliding friction on the grass in the early part of its travel, as explained in Chapter 31.

It is easy to demonstrate this by making such a putt. You will observe that deviation of the ball travel from a straight line is so small it is almost imperceptible. There is very little sidewise curvature due to the cutting motion. It has none of the aerodynamic curvature (hook or slice) which accompanies a long flight from a long club when the ball has side spin.

Trying to cut the ball is another example of a golf stroke having unnecessary additional inputs which add to the errors inherent in the simplest stroke. Additional error sources are the new direction of travel of the head, the amount by which the club face is open, and the needed change in head speed.

Golfers usually succeed with cutting the ball because they use it only for very short putts. Cutting the ball can only degrade the success.

GRAIN OF THE GRASS

Blades of grass tend to lean to one side or another, depending on various things. Possibilities are the direction of the mowing machine, the slope of the green, and perhaps the direction of the sun when the grass is growing fastest.

In tests on a good bentgrass green with our precision putting machine, as described in Chapter 27, no apparent effect was found due to grain of the grass. Bermuda grass may behave differently.

This could be studied more carefully at various directions on an especially level green.

If a golfer corrects for grain and its effect is negligible, another unnecessary additional error is introduced.

Eyes Over the Ball, Keeping the Putter Square

Although the conclusions described here are based on technical considerations, they agree with widely recognized advice on the subject.

Most golfers know they should have their eyes over the ball at address. When your eyes are not over the ball, there is a change of the apparent ideal direction of the swing. Practice can make that okay, only if you can closely repeat this eye position. It is easier to repeat the "eyes over the ball" position than some other, less well defined location.

Various putter features are advertised to assure that your eye is vertically above the putter head, but these claims may be misleading. Typically there is a line or dot low on the putter head and a matching feature higher on the putter head. The upper feature is intended to be located vertically above the lower, from your view point. This only assures that you are looking squarely to the putter head, not that your eye is vertically above the head. To convince yourself, hold such a putter out in front at eye level – you'll still be able to align the 2 aiming features, but your eyes certainly are not vertically above the ball.

The usual conviction of golfers is that they should avoid rotating the putter head during the backswing and the downswing. Rotating the putter head tends to introduce unnecessary additional errors which can be avoided.

General Conclusions

For any golf stroke, there is no logical reason to do things which are not essential, if any of the other things you might do could possibly add additional errors to the basic golfer errors without some important compensating advantage. In other words, "keep it simple."

TECHNICAL NOTES

Your eye, the ball, and the hole are essentially 3 points in space, which according to the fundamental laws of geometry, determine a plane. The 3 points form a triangle in this plane. Your eye is always in this plane because it is at one apex of the triangle.

The entire plane appears to your eye as a line. All 3 points are in this plane and therefore appear to be "in line." This is true, no matter where you place your eye in the plumb-bobbing set-up.

It is easy to erroneously believe that only one eye position puts the points in line. Here is a convincing test to try if you wear eyeglasses. Take a draftsman's triangle and hold one apex against your glasses, immediately in front of one eye, with the other eye closed. No matter how you orient the triangle, the other apexes appear to be in line. Obviously, this is dangerous if you don't have eye protection.

One is tempted to believe that things would be okay if the golfer could somehow make sure the eye and the ball are in a vertical plane. The 2 examples described above show that plumb-bobbing can misguide the golfer, even with any such additional alignment condition. These problems are absent when plumb-bobbing is used only for judging slope.

EFFECTS OF SCUFFING THE GRASS

Y OUR FAIRWAY WOODS ARE DESIGNED TO SKIM THE BALL OFF THE FAIRWAY WITH A NICE TRAJECTORY. YOUR PUTTER IS DESIGNED TO STRIKE THE BALL ALONG THE SURFACE – AND PRODUCE A GROUND-HUGGING ROLL. A SCUFF AFFECTS THE RESULT OF YOUR EFFORT. HOW FREQUENTLY DOES IT HAPPEN? HOW IMPORTANT IS IT? YOU'LL HAVE FUN WITH THIS ONE.

The term "scuff" means that the sole of the putter is below the top of the grass at the time of impact. Nothing has been published about scuffs and their effects on a putt and it appears that scuffs have received little attention.

Average golfers rarely feel a scuff but when strong enough to feel, they observe that it causes a rather drastic loss of distance. If lighter scuffs are not noticed by the golfer, could they still cause a serious loss of distance? If so, they must be regarded as an additional golfer error.

Here are 2 important facts. Most golfers know when they have a serious deep scuff; they learned to avoid them when first learning to putt. At the other extreme, a golfer never whiffs a putt, even when first learning, and almost never tops a putt. This indicates it is much less likely for golfers to swing the putter too high as compared with swinging it too low.

In addition, our many tests with marking tape on the putter face showed that most golfers tend to swing their putters somewhat too low and very few swing somewhat too high. This also suggests that there is more leeway for swinging the putter too high as compared with swinging it too low.

Most golfers may profit by trying to raise the putter a little. This chapter will discuss the effects of scuffs and make suggestions for golfers who may be unaware they have a problem with scuffs.

Our research found that although scuff putts are numerous, most are quite gentle and cause negligible distance errors, particularly for golfers with low HCP. Golfers are unaware of these numerous gentle scuffs, and it rarely matters.

TESTING SCUFFS

We made a test to see when a golfer begins to feel a scuff. We got a good golfer to swing a putter which had a slender wire connecting the putter head with a support point 50 inches above the grass, about the normal location of the center of rotation of a putter. The golfer found that this had little effect on his normal swing.

The support position was adjusted downward in amounts unknown to the golfer until he could feel the scuff. He could not feel a scuff until the sole of the putter was nearly down to the level of the soil (the ground level). The loss of distance of the putt was clearly evident.

This test provided good confirmation of our idea that golfers do not feel slight scuffs. It shows that they are only able to feel scuffs which are so deep that there are serious distance losses.

Our calculations show that the deeper of the imperceptible light scuffs cause significant loss of putt distance, while shallow scuffs, which are far more numerous, cause negligible loss.

EFFECTS OF STIMP

We measured the drag characteristics of grass and how it varies with Stimp and depth of scuffs. The results in Figure 35-1 show the calculated distance losses as percentage of the total putt distance vs. depth of scuff putts below the top of the grass for putt distances of 5, 15, and 45 feet. The tests were made using a currently popular putter on greens with Stimp readings of 7, 9, and 11 feet.

SYMBOLS AND DEFINITIONS	
C_b [] coefficient of friction for ball sliding in grass.	HS [mph] head speed, speed of the cg of the head just prior to impact.
C_f [] coefficient of friction for flat plate sliding in grass.	Stimp, S rating of the green speed*
H [in] span, the vertical distance from lowest to highest position of the clubhead for good shots.	TBB [in] vertical distance, top of grass to bottom of ball.
	* More detail will be found for this item in the Appendix.
HCP handicap.	

The curves on the three drawings show that scuffing causes more loss of distance for short putts than with long putts. Also scuffing causes negligible losses for shallow scuffs and surprisingly large losses for deeper scuffs.

From the figure, it might appear that there is much greater loss of putt distance for greens with high Stimp than for low Stimp. Actually, these graphs do not directly indicate putting success, and their effects on putting success are explained below.

DATA ANALYSIS

Examination of the curves for 5-foot putt distance shows that about 25% of the distance is lost if the sole scuffs are .07 inch deep for Stimp 11, .09 inch deep for Stimp 9, and .14 inch deep for Stimp 7. Stimp 11 is a fast green and Stimp 7 is a rather slow green. The scuffs for 25% distance loss are about 30% deeper for 15-feet putts and about 85% deeper for 45-foot putts, compared to 5-foot putts. Thus, scuffs affect short putts much more than long putts.

Deeper scuffs which cause much distance loss are much less frequent than the shallower scuffs so they are less important than it might seem, as will be explained. Shallow scuffs are not important because they cause little putter drag.

The Technical Notes show how we found that putts should usually be centered about 3/8th inch above the sole of the putter. This leaves a question of how high a golfer's HCP must be before a serious fraction of hits will be down to troublesome depths.

Experiments described in Chapter 28 show that on average, golfers tend to center their hit patterns .2 inch higher than ideal. That means the average putter tends to be .2 inch lower than ideal. Further, this happens with golfers of both low and high HCP.

Table 35-1 portrays Figure 28-3 in a different form. This is for a putter with a rather large sole area and a large radius of curvature of the sole. Putters with narrow soles will sink a little deeper than shown in Table 35-1.

When the hit pattern is centered higher, the sole is lower in the grass; conversely, when the hit pattern is centered lower, the sole is higher in the grass.

Table 35-2 shows the percentage of putter hits at HCP of 0, 15, and 30, which are below the top of the grass for golfers who center their putts low, average, and high, based on Table 35-1. This percentage

depends on HCP because, unlike the height of the centers, the scatter of hits up and down on the face depends on HCP and is greater with higher HCP.

Therefore, golfers who center their hit patterns higher than ideal will have more frequent and more serious scuffs and golfers who center their patterns lower will have fewer.

With this information, it is clear that scuffs deserve your attention if you center your hits high (meaning the sole is low), as most golfers do, and if your HCP is above 5 or 10.

SEVERITY OF SCUFFS

A more useful way to understand the effects of putts is given in Table 35-3. Here you find the percentages of putts which lose distances of 5% or more.

Scuffs which cause less distance loss are relatively unimportant, so we arbitrarily consider scuffs to be negligible if they lose less than this percentage. We apply the term "scuff putt" to scuffs which lose more than 5% of the distance.

At putt distances of 5, 15 and 45 feet, 5% losses amount to 3, 9, and 27 inches respectively. The percentages in Table 35-3 demonstrates that scuff putts are more frequent and cause more distance errors than is commonly realized.

Remember that Table 35-3 is for average height of the center of the pattern. Golfers who center their patterns higher have the putter lower and have larger scuffing errors. In tests, the golfer could only feel scuffs when they caused errors much larger than 5% of the distance.

IMPROVING YOUR PUTTING

As explained above, some golfers sometimes notice severe scuffs, but almost no golfers notice they have topped the ball when they putt. (Topping means the bottom of the putter face hits above the center of the ball.) It appears that topping a putt is about as easy to notice as a severe scuff.

Since topping is almost never noticed, we conclude that many or most golfers could putt with the putter at least somewhat higher than they usually do with no significant problem of topping the putt. Topping, unlike scuffing, doesn't depend on the Stimp of the green. From these considerations, we suggest:

Golfers might experiment to find how high they can

lift their putters before they begin to notice topping putts once in every 10 or 20 putts. If this is a noticeable increase in putter height, they should try to lift the putter a little higher than usual while putting, but not as high as the topping experiment.

Ideally, this would significantly improve putting distance accuracy, especially for higher HCP golfers and also for golfers of rather low HCP, who may tend to center their hits rather high on the putter face. It does not help to choose a putter having a deeper face (higher from top to bottom).

Note that this improvement will be hard to detect unless you are in the habit of carefully recording the number of putts in each round.

EXPERIMENTS ON PUTTER HEIGHT

This brings up the question of how high a golfer lifts the putter before impact. Most golfers sole their putters and start their backswing from that starting position. They may not be clearly aware of when they move it upward prior to impact, nor how high they move it.

Try this and you will find that no matter how you determine the height of your putter, you are easily able to raise your putter until you begin to top putts. Thus, your experiments at finding how high to lift the putter may consist of deliberately topping putts and deliberately scuffing to give a feeling of what is midway between.

For most putter designs, your target is to center impacts about 3/8 inch above the putter sole. For putters whose face height is less than 3/4 inch, center your impacts halfway up the face. See the Technical Notes for more explanation.

The suggested adjustment can be accomplished in another way which you might prefer: Try to swing your putter a little higher, to see if you begin topping the putts. If not, swing it still higher. When you find the height which causes slight topping, lower it somewhat and use that position.

Thereafter, if you detect topping, swing it still lower. Most golfers probably did approximately the same thing without thinking about it when they learned to putt, but it is worth review. A third way to find out how high to lift your putter is to use marking tape on the putter face. Make numerous putts and putter height adjustments until the marking tapes

show that your average hit is about 3/8 inch above the sole.

In summary, it is hard to detect the onset of errors until a very serious scuff happens. Our research suggests that many golfers should raise their putters slightly higher.

Chapter 36 shows how putter accuracy can be rated with and without consideration of scuffs.

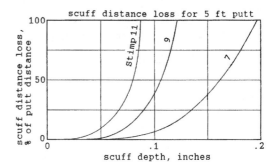

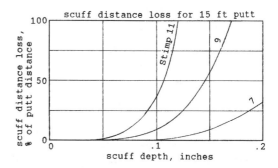

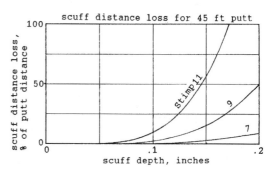

Fig. 35-1 *Distance loss as a percent of total putt distance vs. scuff depth for Stimp 7, 9, and 11 as marked on each curve. Scuff depth is measured from the top of the grass.*

Table 35-1 *Effect of Stimp (S) on the height of the center of the hit pattern. The "high" column refers to golfers who average 1/16" above average position; average is the average for all golfers tested; and "low" refers to golfers who average 1/16" low.*

Stimp	center height, in		
	high	average	low
S7	.65	.59	.53
S9	.69	.62	.56
S11	.70	.64	.57

Table 35-2 *The effect of Stimp (S) and HCP on the % of hits which are below the top of grass. Table 35-1 defines low, average, and high pattern centers.*

	high			average			low		
HCP: 0	15	30	0	15	30	0	15	30
S7	81.8	72.1	67.9	38.5	41.8	43.7	7.1	16.6	24.0
S9	43.1	45.0	46.1	8.6	19.2	25.5	.6	4.6	9.5
S11	25.5	31.7	35.4	3.4	9.9	17.5	.1	2.3	5.9

Table 35-3 *The percentage of putts which are scuff putts, defined as putts for which scuffs cause loss of more than 5% of the putt distance for various Stimp, marked "S". For putt distances of 5, 15, and 45 feet, these respective 5% losses are 3, 9, and 27 inches. This applies to the average height of the center of the pattern (Table 35-1).*

	putt distance, ft: 5			15			45		
HCP: 0	15	30	0	15	30	0	15	30
S7	1.9	7.2	13.9	.2	2.9	7.4	.0	.4	3
S9	.5	4.3	9.2	.1	2.3	6.1	.0	.6	3.5
S11	.2	3.4	7.7	.1	2.1	5.8	.0	.6	3.8

TECHNICAL NOTES

The research process to analyze scuffs was rather complex. We calculated the drag force and loss of distance for a typical, popular putter for greens of various Stimp, based on measurements of various characteristics of grass on putting greens.

Stiffness of grass was measured for various Stimp readings by simply applying various small loads to an aluminum disk 1.25 inches diameter and recording its downward movement. The measurement requires a definition of the top of the grass; we found this by placing a thin, flat aluminum shim (.006 inch thick and usually 1 by 3 inches) on the grass and the shim caused negligible downward movement.

We expressed the pressure-deflection relation for grass in a least-squares fitted empirical equation. Here, S is Stimp [ft], d is grass deflection [in], P is the pressure on the grass [pounds/square inch], and $n = 5.17 - .176*S$.

$$P = (-5.43 + .776*S)*d + (-6960 + 1144*S)*d^n \ [psi]$$

This equation applies over a range of pressure from zero to 5 psi and Stimp from 7.8 to 9.4 and probably wider. These pressures were sufficient to press the grass from slight deformation until the aluminum disk was tight against the soil, at which point the soil begins to deform.

We measured force for sliding a plate on grass for various loads on the plate. From the total weight and the force, we found the coefficient of sliding friction for a flat plate, Cf. Cf is reasonably well represented as a constant which applies over a range of Stimp from about 2 or 3 to 11 feet:

$$Cf = .796 \ []$$

For the measurements, we used a pair of drag rails, essentially two flat plates, each .5" by 6", mounted parallel and 5 inches apart under a thin aluminum sheet with various loads on top. On these rails, we provided various edge radii from about .02 inch to .1 inch.

Drag force on the rails was about the same when dragged perpendicular to the length of the rails or when dragged parallel to the rails, regardless of the depth, Stimp, and edge radius. From this, we concluded that edge radius didn't matter, at least within this range of radii.

We used rails made of both polished and finely sanded aluminum. We also used rails having polyethylene, teflon, and vinyl surfaces. There was little difference in drag forces among these materials.

This value of Cf is somewhat different from Cb (the friction coefficient for a ball sliding in the grass as explained in Chapter 27). For the flat plate, average pressure of the grass on the plate is constant over the area and thus independent of Stimp. For a ball, pressure varies under the ball in a way which depends on depth of the grass (indicated by Stimp). According to these tests, Cb = Cf when Stimp is 7.14.

The tests on grass gave considerable scatter, so we took averages of 3 to 6 readings at each of numerous test conditions. More such tests would be interesting for various grass conditions, such as damp and rather dry grass, Bermuda grass, etc.

Chapter 28 discussed the scatter of ball impacts on the putter face, which shows how scatter depends on HCP. Those impacts which are high in the pattern mean the putter sole is low.

The centers of each impact allow the corresponding depth in the grass to be calculated. To do so requires knowing the height of the center of the ball when the ball is resting in the grass.

The distance from the top of the grass to the bottom of the ball, or TBB, was measured by placing a ball on the grass and finding the separation between 2 of the .006 inch shims when they were gently placed parallel against opposite sides of the ball. Their separation allowed calculation of the depth of the bottom of the ball. The depth is expressed empirically as:

$$TBB = 27.2 * S^{(-2.54)} \ [in]$$

This equation applies from Stimp 7.8 to 9.4 and is probably suitable for a wider range.

The first 2 tests make it practical to calculate the drag force required to slide the sole of a putter through the grass, for various depths.

The scatter of impacts allows calculation of corresponding depths of the sole into the grass, so we can find how often and how deep putts occur which scuff the grass for various Stimp and HCP. This provides the basis for calculating the energy lost due to drag friction during each putt, and from this, the loss of distance of the putt due to drag for any putt distance, Stimp, and scuff depth.

The calculation of distance error used a rather complicated analysis integrating the drag forces over various putter sole geometries, as the putter moved from the first contact with the grass, up to impact through an arc with 50 inch radius. These calculations yield the drag work.

The putter head speed (HS) and weight define the kinetic energy after HS is found from the putt distance equations of Chapter 27. The drag work reduced this energy to give HS at impact. In this way, HS without drag compared to HS with drag allowed us to calculate the distance error caused by putter drag, using the putt distance equation.

One rather surprising result was that we found that neither the sole area nor its geometry had large effects on the scuffing problem.

The ideal height to center impacts on a putter with 3-degree loft was calculated, ignoring scuffs which lose less than 5% of the distance. For 15-foot putts, the idea height is .39 inch at Stimp 9, provided the putter face is at least .78 inch high.

The ideal height for centering with a putter is found from calculating span H for putters in the same way described in Chapter 24 for other clubs. Hits which are centered higher are more prone to scuffs, and if centered lower, are prone to topping the putt.

For higher Stimp, hits should be slightly lower but the effect is small. Loft angle between 0 and 6 degrees alters this only slightly. Putter faces should be at least .78 inch high. If less, the hit pattern should be centered, top-to bottom.

PERFORMANCE RATING OF PUTTERS

Here, you're in for a real surprise: putter design has very little effect on success of your putts! One putter is as good as another. Let's see about this.

The computer model allows calculation of the scatter of stop points for putters on level greens in much the same way as for other clubs. Included were errors dTA, dAA, dSA, dLA, dHS, irregularities of the green, and in some cases, scuffing errors. Errors of the golfer in reading sloping greens were not measured or included.

Golfers usually try to avoid rotating the wrists during the swing on a putt. For this reason, we believe that unintended wrist rotation is small for putters. Any such rotation is reflected in the value of dTA. Mostly, these golfer errors vary with HCP and such effects are included in the calculation of stop points.

We defined a rating for putters, which we call PHO (for putts to hole out) for a golfer of HCP 15 with 15-foot putts on a level green of Stimp 9. For every putt which failed to hole out (stopping in the hole zone, the remaining putts needed to hole out was calculated.

This process was done for 10,000 putts, each resulting from randomly sampling the statistical distributions of values of dTA, dAA, dHS, dLA, dSA, and green irregularities. The allowed us to calculate the average PHO for all of these putts, as further discussed in the Technical Notes.

Table 36-1 gives this putter rating for Putters A and R for HCP 15 in bold type and includes similar calculations for HCP 0 and 30 for comparison. The differences between results for Putters A and R are less than .01 putt and do not show in the table.

As will be discussed, HCP, Stimp, or putt distance would not change the ranking between the putters. The bold values in the table for HCP 15 are approximations of the average golfer putting the average first-putt distance on good greens. This is what we use for the PHO putter rating.

We also found that when scuffs were considered, there was little change in Table 36-1 and no change in the ranking. Putter A in the table is our Model 330 putter which was optimized. Putter R, while technically a relatively poor putter design, is pleasing in appearance and has been popular for many years. Its cg is much too high and its moments of inertia are small, increasing the errors for off-center hits as discussed in Chapter 33.

The PHO process shows that these deficiencies are unimportant because the table shows no difference between Putter A and Putter R.

Other kinds of ratings were tried as discussed in the Technical Notes, but the ratings shown there are not as meaningful as PHO. Since a golfer is only concerned with putts to hole out, the slight performance differences are unimportant and those other kinds of ratings are less satisfactory.

Some rating calculations were also made of an imaginary modification of Putter A in which the face

SYMBOLS AND DEFINITIONS

AA alignment angle.*
AD [in] aim distance, the optimum distance beyond the center of the hole for aiming a putt.
dAA [deg] standard deviation of AA.
dHS [%] standard deviation of HS just before impact as a percent of HS.
dLA [in] standard deviation of the center of impact locations (hit patterns) on the club face, measured in the direction of the long axis of the impact pattern. dLA is approximately in the toe-heel direction.
dSA [in] the same as dLA but measured in the direction of the short axis of the hit pattern and is approximately in the up-down direction.
dTA [deg] standard deviation of TA.
HCP handicap.

HS [mph] head speed, speed of the cg of the head just prior to impact.
LA loft angle.*
ME [in for putts, otherwise yd] most probable error of stop points, taken to be the average error, measured from the stop point of an error-free center hit.
MRD [in] mean radial distance from the center of the hole, rather than from the aim point.
PHO [ ] putts needed to hole out.
putter A an optimized design, our model 330.
putter R a popular design with low moments of inertia and cg which is much too high.
TA [deg] target angle for putters, as defined in Figure 27-1.

* More detail will be found for these items in the Appendix.

was assumed to have a roll radius of .75 inch. The modified putter had a slightly poorer rating which is explained further in the Technical Notes.

To summarize, Table 36-1 and additional detail in the Technical Notes support a surprising conclusion: There is negligible difference in performance between what is representative of the best and the poorest of conventional putter designs.

Putter choice is unimportant except for factors such as appearance, familiarity, and subjective personal preference of golfers. It seems that in most cases, golfers should stay with whatever putter head, shaft, and face surface they may prefer and be confident that technically, it is okay.

This appears to be consistent with reports of some tour professionals who continue for many years to favor an old putter which they like.

This work shows that scatter of putts over the face of a putter (hit pattern error) has only a small effect on the scatter of stop points and therefore on PHO. This is because dAA, dHS, variations of greens, and green-reading errors predominate and almost completely mask hit pattern errors.

As has been explained, errors of stop points generally do not simply add together – larger errors mask smaller errors. The smaller errors rapidly diminish to negligible importance for putters as they become smaller than roughly 25% to 10% of the largest errors.

A direct consequence is that an advertising claim of reducing some small error is nearly a worthless claim, even if it is true (earlier, with respect to putters, we too were guilty). To be significant, differences in design must appreciably reduce the PHO rating or some equivalent measure of performance which reasonably accounts for all of the most important errors.

Putter design can't reduce scatter caused by errors other than hit pattern errors, dLA and dSA. The Technical Notes discuss comparison of the 2 putters for 3 other rating methods and supports our decision to use PHO.

For other clubs, hit patterns are larger, moments of inertia of the head are much smaller, and aerodynamic effects increase errors for off-center hits. This causes appreciable differences of performance among various designs, unlike the conclusion for putters.

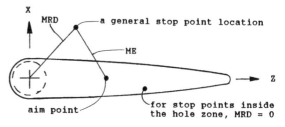

Fig. 36-1 *The hole zone and how it is used to define ME, MRD, and % made.*

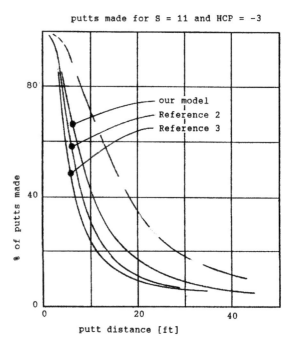

Fig. 36-2 *Comparison of % made for putts according to our model and two similar sets which were measured on professional golfers in actual play. Our results are for Stimp 11 and HCP-3. The dashed curve show our results when green imperfections are omitted.*

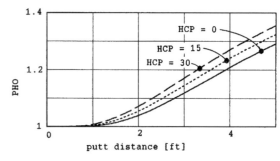

Fig. 36-3 *Putts to hole out, PHO, on level greens of Stimp 9. These curves were calculated from the model and agree well with Reference 2 for similar measurements on golfers.*

Table 36-1 *Comparison of putter accuracy ratings, based on PHO, the number of putts to hole out at 15 foot putt distance and Stimp 9. We chose HCP 15 as the standard; the other lines are for comparison. Putter A is our model 330 which is an optimized design. Putter R is a popular design with lower moments of inertia and cg much too high. There is no significant difference.*

	PHO putter rating	
HCP	putter A	putter R
0	1.78	1.78
15	**1.84**	**1.84**
30	1.90	1.90

Table 36-2 *Various ways to rate putters. Putts were simulated 10,000 times for each entry and average results are tabulated here for Stimp 7. Table 36-3 is the same except for Stimp 11. "Dist" is putt distance, ft. ME means the mean variation in inches from the mean stop point. MRD means the mean remaining putt distance in inches for putts which did not drop. "% made" is the % of successful putts. Values in bold italics, are results when scuffing is considered.*

		putter A						putter R				
dist.	HCP	ME		MRD		% made		ME		MRD		% made
5	0	3.50	*3.54*	11.02	*11.04*	68.0	*67.9*	3.31	*3.49*	7.36	*7.40*	68.0	*67.9*
5	15	4.66	*5.67*	8.69	*9.35*	65.9	*62.4*	4.68	*5.87*	8.57	*9.60*	66.0	*62.3*
5	30	6.27	*9.14*	11.90	*14.48*	57.6	*52.7*	6.30	*9.56*	11.67	*14.88*	57.8	*52.5*
15	0	9.58	*9.62*	14.14	*13.92*	26.2	*26.1*	9.61		14.02		26.2	
15	15	13.26	*13.69*	16.04	*15.95*	19.6	*19.2*	13.31		15.87		19.4	
15	30	16.86	*18.76*	18.48	*19.91*	15.0	*14.2*	16.93		18.30		14.9	
45	0	27.36	*27.36*	28.14	*28.11*	4.8	*4.8*	27.42		28.12		4.8	
45	15	37.73	*37.85*	38.51	*38.65*	3.1	*3.1*	37.85		38.63		3.0	
45	30	48.52	*49.23*	49.42	*50.21*	2.2	*2.2*	48.71		49.61		2.1	

Table 36-3 *This is the same as Table 36-2 except it is for Stimp 11.*

		putter A						putter R				
dist.	HCP	ME		MRD		% made		ME		MRD		% made
5	0	3.33	*3.37*	8.17	*8.18*	72.5	*72.3*	3.33	*3.39*	8.13	*8.19*	72.6	*72.4*
5	15	4.70	*5.49*	9.38	*10.46*	65.1	*63.2*	4.71	*5.87*	9.26	*10.94*	65.3	*63.1*
5	30	6.40	*9.41*	13.47	*17.27*	57.5	*54.0*	6.42	*9.56*	13.24	*17.62*	57.6	*53.6*
15	0	9.66	*9.68*	16.24	*16.22*	27.1	*27.1*	9.67		16.12		27.0	
15	15	13.43	*14.10*	18.20	*18.56*	22.8	*22.3*	13.46		17.95		22.6	
15	30	17.33	*21.60*	21.10	*25.09*	18.1	*17.3*	17.38		20.79		17.9	
45	0	27.28	*27.29*	28.27	*28.27*	6.0	*6.0*	27.31		28.18		5.9	
45	15	37.57	*37.98*	38.21	*38.61*	4.0	*4.0*	37.65		38.24		3.9	
45	30	47.93	*51.49*	48.93	*52.71*	3.0	*2.9*	48.06		49.09		2.8	

TECHNICAL NOTES

Four ways were considered to rate the performance of putters, each based on a different way to measure and rate accuracy of putts. Putts to hole out (PHO) was discussed above and is shown in Table 36-1.

Figure 36-1 illustrates 2 other ways, using ME and MRD. First, an aim point beyond the center of the hole (as discussed in Chapter 32) is assumed.

ME is the mean of the radial distances from this aim point as if the hole was covered, and considers stop points, both inside and outside of the hole zone.

MRD is the mean radial distance from the center of the hole, rather than from the aim point, and considers only the putts which stopped outside the hole zone, the others being successful putts.

The 4th way performance rating was tested is "% made," found by tallying the total of stop points inside the hole zone, and expressing this as a percentage of the total number of putts.

The long, slender nature of the hole zone outline was defined by equations in Chapter 30. This shape means that for level greens, distance errors are far less important for putting success than are lateral errors. This has a strong influence on deciding which kind of rating is most meaningful and useful.

For example, dHS has the largest effect on scatter of the stop points as is measured by ME; whereas if dHS causes distance errors much shorter than the length of the hole zone, it would have little or no effect on the success of putts. MRD and % made reduce this problem, but the most useful and meaningful measure to a golfer is the average number of putts which will be required to hole out, PHO. MRD and % made do not indicate that directly.

Figure 36-2 compares % made (as calculated) with directly measured % made from the indicated references for golf professionals on real greens. Our % made (and other ratings) is for flat greens and does not consider errors associated with reading the Stimp or the slope of the green. If these two factors are included, they would cause more errors than indicated by our % made and would therefore lower our curve, likely into closer agreement with the measured data.

This agreement tends to confirm the validity of our computer model. We would have made this comparison for other ratings we studied, but did not find any published data for golfers for PHO, MRD, and ME. Figure 36-3 shows how HCP affects PHO for short putts.

Tables 36-2 and 36-3 give the ME, MRD, and % made ratings at various distances and handicaps (HCP) with two different Stimp ratings. The accuracy of the 2nd decimal place is doubtful. The numbers in italics include the effects of scuffs, discussed in Chapter 35. The others ignore scuffs.

We gave most attention to the 15-foot putts because this is approximately the average distance for a golfer's first putt.

In Table 36-3, with Stimp 11 for Putter A, notice that 15-foot putts for HCP 15 have a difference in ME for the scuff and no-scuff cases of only .67 inch for ME and .36 inch for MRD. This difference is greater for 5-foot putts (.79 and 1.08 inch) and smaller for 45 foot putts (.41 and .40 inch). That is because a scuff loses the same amount of energy for short and long putts and thus causes a larger effect for short putts.

The % made columns also show similar small differences due to scuffs. This supports our conclusion that scuffs are a minor effect, except for high HCP golfers, especially when the average center of putts is high (sole is low) and for short putts.

For HCP 15 at 15-foot putt distance, ME for putter R is only .05 inch greater than for putter A. MRD differs by .25 inch. These numbers tend to be smaller for smaller HCP and larger for larger HCP. These comparisons are about the same for Stimp 7.

The calculation process was to find the HS for each putter type to give desired AD. Then 10,000 more putts were made with normally distributed random values of the errors.

For those putts having scuffs, the kinetic energy of the putter for the given HS was reduced by the amount of the drag energy loss. Severe scuffs are so rare they contribute less to the average result than might be expected.

This study of the nature of the other 3 ratings was useful to show more about their behavior and to compare putters. PHO remains the preferred rating, however.

Part Five

A SUMMARY

NEW AND USEFUL RESULTS OF OUR RESEARCH

KNOW AND AVOID YOUR MOST DEADLY ERRORS. LEARN BETTER ORGANIZED TECHNIQUES. PUTTERS ARE ALL EQUALLY GOOD, BUT FOR OTHER CLUBS, ESPECIALLY DRIVERS, SOME DESIGNS ARE REALLY BETTER. WE HOPE THIS BOOK IS USEFUL TO YOU!

We developed a mathematical model of club-ball impact, flight, bounce and roll. We programmed it in computers and used it extensively to study numerous aspects of golf shots and to find optimized club designs. We did much field work to measure golfer errors, characteristics of the turf, and other things which we found to be required inputs for this model. We expect that any future refinements in the model and our data inputs will not greatly change these conclusions.

This research led to several new and surprising conclusions about the use and design of golf clubs. Some agree well with current design trends and some are distinctly at odds. Here are the highlights of our research. Most are further described in the later sections of this chapter.

- For drivers, an extra large face provides important advantages by reducing hits which are partly off the face.

- For drivers, and to some extent the other clubs, a computer-generated face surface shape (surface curvature) can reduce scatter of stop points enough to be noticeable to golfers.

- There is an optimum combination of LA and cg location for maximum CHD for any given driver shaft and clubhead weight.

- Light, stiff shafts are important to realize maximum CHD and grip weight has very little effect.

- There is an optimum combination of shaft length, shaft weight, and head weight for maximum CHD.

- There is a simple, detailed aiming procedure which should improve accuracy. It provides excellent control of slices and hooks. We call it "regripping". It is much like most modern aiming procedures, but differs in essential details.

- There is a similar procedure for best aiming of putters, but with certain essential differences.

- Careful use of the model for putters shows that there are no significant differences in performance among most currently available putters.

- Our model facilitates a wide variety of examples of the effects of atmospheric and turf conditions, and of club design parameters.

SYMBOLS AND DEFINITIONS

AA [deg] alignment angle, the angle between the path of the clubhead.

cg center of gravity (more accurately, center of mass); its location is usually given in inches.

CHD [yd] center hit distance (more accurately, the distance of a hit at the face center with no golfer errors, including the flight {carry}, bounce and roll, for our reference ball under reference atmospheric conditions, on a representative level fairway.)

CLG [in] club length (more accurately, measured from the top of the grip to the intersection of the shaft axis with the X-Z plane when the club is held at the address position.)

dAA [deg] standard deviation of AA.

dHS [%] standard deviation of HS just before impact as a percent of HS.

dLA [in] standard deviation of the center of impact locations (hit patterns) on the club face, measured in the direction of the long axis of the impact pattern. dLA is approximately in the toe-heel direction.

dSA [in] the same as dLA but measured in the direction of the short axis of the hit pattern and is approximately in the up-down direction.

dWA [deg] for a golfer, the standard deviation of the rotation about the butt-head-cg axis from its mean value. It is approximately rotation around the shaft's long axis. It is also about the same as standard deviation of WA and FS for putters.

FS [deg] face-shaft angle which a golfer may adjust to control hooks and slices (see Figure 25-4).

HCP handicap.

HS [mph] head speed, speed of the cg of the head just prior to impact.

LA [deg] loft angle (see Appendix).

POF hits partly off the face hits for those hits near the edge of the face for which more than 25% of the imprint is off the face.

OPTIMIZING CLUB DESIGN

The optimum design of golf clubs should be consistent with the "Rules of Golf" established by the United States Golf Association. We believe such rules are reasonable and desirable and that within these rules, only limited further performance improvement is possible beyond the optimized designs we developed.

For drivers, the principal improvements which we made come from the optimum combination of cg location; moments of inertia; loft angle; shaft length; head weight; head size and face size; face outline shape and orientation; and shape of the face surface. The optimum combination provides significant reduction of scatter of stop points, and gains a little on CHD.

The improved accuracy for drivers is enough to be perceptible to golfers, as compared with other modern designs; at the same time, an optimum design gains a little in distance of center hits. Golfer experience on production models confirms the computer-model results; their most common report is "fewer drives off the fairway."

Some examples are given with irons using the same process, but not all research which might be applicable was completed.

For putters, we reached the surprising conclusion that performance differences among modern putters is negligible, including designs we have produced.

SHAFT MATERIALS

Regarding shafts for maximum distance clubs (drivers and the first fairway woods), the best choice is any good, lightweight graphite shaft for which the lower 20 or 30% is reasonably stiff. Older, heavier shafts for these clubs, such as steel, cause an important, easily noticed loss of CHD. Larger than usual shaft diameter is structurally advantageous.

We have found no direct significance for such things as location of the "kick" point, vibration frequency, and bulges in the shaft. Such things do not necessarily relate to the desired features of low shaft weight and large tip stiffness, for which numerical values are necessary for optimized design.

Good driver shafts of titanium are presently available but weigh significantly more than graphite shafts and thus reduce maximum CHD. Steel is distinctly worse. These observations apply to the maximum distance clubs.

Shaft material and design for the other clubs are relatively uncritical, though the higher stiffness which is practical for steel shafts provides a small advantage. For these other clubs, shaft weight is unimportant because a longer club can always be chosen when more distance is needed. All modern shafts work about equally well for irons, and personal preference is the main factor in making a choice.

Grip weight is of minor importance. A very light grip on a driver will cause gain of CHD of only one yard or less, when compared to a heavy grip such as an "arthritic" grip on an otherwise identical driver. A consequence is that shafts with extra large butts and light-weight grips provide little advantage in CHD.

CLUB FACE DESIGN AND CHOICE OF MATERIAL

Appropriate use of our model revealed a marked improvement in the shape of the face surface, as compared with the usual bulge and roll radii of faces for woods. It reduces the scatter of stop points caused by off-center hits, to a perceptible extent as described in Chapter 18.

We found an important advantage, namely reducing POF hits, for drivers by using a very large face whose outline and orientation approximate the pattern of hits by golfers. However, maximum size is limited by the head becoming structurally too weak if too large. Extra-large faces also have a small CHD penalty due to air drag during the swing. Strength of available materials and air drag limit face size to about the largest sizes we have described.

There is no particular advantage, and may even be a slight disadvantage, to using titanium for driver heads. Aluminum alloys are not as stiff or strong as titanium. Being much less dense, the face can be thicker, and the result is somewhat favorable to aluminum for a given head weight. Magnesium is still lighter, but much less strong. Cast aluminum is as satisfactory as titanium and perhaps slightly better. Cast steel or stainless steel is a poorer choice than aluminum or titanium.

Maximum size (and particularly, large face size) is strongly conducive to large inertia values and fewer POF hits.

Concentrated weights of copper or even tungsten in certain "magic" locations is generally not advantageous because they tend to reduce the maximum head size. The reason is that for maximum size, the material of the body must be distributed to provide suitable cg location, large face size, maximum moments of inertia, and adequate strength, leaving little or none for concentrated weights.

We analyzed the penalty on CHD caused by air drag on the head and shaft during the swing. This showed that modern large heads and large shafts contribute about equally to air drag, but cause no more than about 1-yard loss of CHD.

Improved face surface curvature, large face size, and large moments of inertia provide minimum scatter of stop points and more tolerance for off-center hits. Such designs are more forgiving and easier to hit.

TESTS WITH GOLFERS, GOLFERS' ERRORS

We made systematic tests of HS with a wide variety of golfers. Each used a test set of 9 drivers of various club lengths and head weights. First HS was measured, then the optimum cg location and loft angle for each hit was calculated to find the corresponding CHD. The ultimate design for distance has a very light shaft and grip.

Optimum CLG was 50.3 inches with 192 gram head, and this depended little on golfer gender, height, or ability. Because this length is unsuitable for most golfers, we chose a rather stiff, light, 46 inch graphite shaft and 194 gram head weight to be a good compromise. This shorter shaft, and heavier head than ideal for that shaft, was close enough to provide center hit distance within a few yards of the ultimate.

No driver design can gain more than about 2 or 3 yards over this practical compromise. Potential distance gain for a given golfer depends little on his strength and skill level.

This contrasts with putters where there is negligible difference in performance among current designs, with no prospect of improvement.

We conducted many other tests with golfers to measure their various errors. Of these, our model showed that for drivers, the most important errors are dHS, dAA, dWA, dLA, and dSA.

POF hits can cause very large errors for golfers of average or higher handicap.

Good design for drivers can reduce the frequency of these POF hits, improve CHD, and can slightly reduce the errors of wrist angle (clubhead orientation at impact). No design features of a club can reduce head speed variation which is usually the most important golfer error for all clubs except for putters. However, good design can reduce the effects of scatter of hits over the club face (the hit pattern, dLA and dSA).

PUTTERS

For putters, the most important error is clubhead orientation. Proper alignment of the swing path and proper head speed are next in importance. Design can do little or nothing to reduce scatter caused by these 3 errors.

Nearly all golfers have slight scuffs on some putts which cause negligible errors. However, golfers who tend to center their hits high on the face may have unnoticed small errors due to scuffing, particularly if they have high HCP. Ways to reduce this possibility are discussed.

Surprisingly, off-center hits with putters cause negligible errors compared with the other errors. The result is negligible difference in performance among putter designs.

AIMING

For all clubs, erroneous clubhead orientation at impact is a large, or the largest, golfer error. Clubhead orientation deserves close attention.

In summary, for aiming all clubs except the putter and chip shots, the sequence is: first, to get straight shots, choose the appropriate club face orientation with respect to your hands, with no regard for the target direction, then take your grip; second, without changing your grip, choose the appropriate club face orientation relative to the direction you want by adjusting your stance (the turntable idea) as required.

This process leads to straight shots, whether or not the swing is good, if the golfer learns the appropriate clubhead orientation for straight shots by practicing his regripping process. Modifying the face orientation from the "straight shot" orientation allows controlled draws and fades (hooks and slices).

For putters and short chip shots, the aiming process should be different. It is best done by first choosing the best stance orientation relative to the target direction which is different from the hole direction if break is expected. Then the putter face is chosen to be square to the target direction.

One reason for the difference is that wrists must rotate during the swing for long hits but most golfers try to avoid wrist rotation in the putting stroke. Another reason is that erroneous face orientation at impact causes side spin on the ball. That has little effect for putts but curves the long shots and increases the lateral error.

Golfer errors could be measured more extensively and with greater precision than we have done, but results are likely to make only small improvements in design. The measurements made are far better than rough estimates or complete lack of data, and we believe they are reasonably adequate.

We studied the effect on the stop point of many combinations of errors. In every case, 1 to 3 of the input errors which cause the largest output errors, mask or "swamp out" effects of all other input errors. This is also typical of error analysis on most other systems.

This masking effect leads to the conclusion that many or most improvements in golf club design yield such small improvements that they are essentially of no value to the golfer.

The significant improvements in the history of golf are limited to the several steps of improvement in golf balls; modern large, metal heads with large moments of inertia; large faces; improved face surface curvature for woods; longer, light shafts for drivers and the first fairway woods; and few other things.

TECHNICAL NOTES

If you are a club designer or a scientifically oriented golfer, you will find discussions, equations and technical detail of the research that are explained in the Technical Notes which are part of most chapters. Testing results provide the basis for the analysis and suggestions described, and should be useful to those concerned with the basic physics and engineering of golf and golf clubs.

Only the fundamentals of our model are described. The computer code for the full model, and its proper use are beyond the scope of this book. We found that a great deal of time was necessary to write, to learn to operate the program, and to use it to best advantage.

APPENDIX

DEFINITIONS

For easy reference, most definitions are repeated in boxes at the beginning of the chapters where they are used. In some cases, definitions in this appendix are more complete and accurate than those summarized at the beginnings of chapters. A few others are defined only in the Technical Notes where they appear.

AA [deg] alignment angle, the angle between the path of the clubhead at impact and the target direction, positive toward the left (more precisely, it is the angle between the target direction and the intersection of the swing plane with the horizontal plane, positive to the left of the target.)

AD [in] aim distance, the optimum distance beyond the center of the hole for aiming a putt.

AHP [deg] angle of the hit pattern, upward tilt of the long axis of the hit pattern (more specifically, the angle of the long axis below the X-Z plane in the head frame). AHP is normally negative.

AR [yd] accuracy rating for drivers which includes the effects of DE and ME.

ARP [yd] like AR except POF effects are included–MEP replaces ME.

bCHD [yd] the increase of CHD when the ball is moved back in the stance with no change in HS or other inputs.

BG [in] ball-ground, clearance from bottom of the ball to the ground (the soil under the ball).

BR [in] bulge radius, the radius of curvature of a club face in the toe-heel direction.

CA [deg] contact angle which is the acute angle between the direction of travel of the clubhead cg and a level plane at the time of impact, measured in the swing plane, and positive when the cg is moving upward.

Cb [ ] coefficient of friction for ball sliding in grass.

CBS [in] vertical distance, bottom of ball to sole of putter.

Cd [ ] aerodynamic drag coefficient of the ball.

Cf [ ] coefficient of friction for flat plate sliding in grass.

cg center of gravity (more accurately, center of mass); its location in the XYZ coordinates is usually given in inches.

CHD [yd] center hit distance (more accurately, the

distance of a hit at the face center with no golfer errors, including the flight or carry, bounce, and roll, for our reference ball under reference atmospheric conditions, on a representative level fairway.)

Cl [ ] aerodynamic lift coefficient of the ball.

CLG [in] club length, measured from the top of the grip to the intersection of the shaft axis with the X-Z plane when the club is held at the address position.

coordinate systems refer to the head frame and the fairway frame definitions. X, Y, and Z coordinates are not the same in these 2 frames of reference. Our model also uses numerous other coordinate systems, not essential in this book.

dA [deg] the standard deviation of putts with all errors present.

dAA [deg] the standard deviation of AA.

Db [in] diameter of the ball.

DE [yd] distance error, the distance by which a given driver's shot stops short of the CHD for reference D driver. In some cases DE uses other reference drivers as identified in such cases.

DD [in] dig distance, distance the bottom of the face of a club digs into the soil.

dFS [deg] standard deviation of FS.

dGA [deg] standard deviation of angular errors in putting due solely to imperfections of the green (equation, Chapter 29).

dGR [ft] standard deviation of distance errors in putting due solely to imperfections of the green (equation, Chapter 29).

dHS [%] standard deviation of HS just before impact as a percent of HS.

dLA [in] standard deviation of the scatter of impact locations (hit patterns) on the club face, measured in the direction of the long axis of the impact pattern. dLA is approximately in the toe-heel direction.

dR [in] standard deviation of putt distance with all errors present.

DR [ft] roll distance of a putt, after sliding has ceased.

drivers A, B, C, D see Table 17-1.

dSA [in] the same as dLA but measured in the direction of the short axis of the hit pattern and is approximately in the up-down direction.

dTA [deg] standard deviation of TA.

dWA [deg] for a golfer, the standard deviation of the rotation about the butt-head-cg axis from its mean value. It is approximately a rotation around the shaft's long axis. It is also about the same as standard deviation of FS for putters.

dX [in] standard deviation of lateral putt distance with all errors present.

FA [deg] face angle. FA is measured in the X-Z plane of the head frame and is the angle between the Z axis and the projection on the X-Z plane of a perpendicular to the face at the face center.

FAE [deg] effective FA, somewhat different from FA because centrifugal force bends the shaft and at impact, and somewhat changes clubhead orientation; CA and wrist rotation also affect FAE.

fairway frame the right hand rectangular coordinate system with origin at the ball center at impact in which the Y axis is vertical, the Z axis points at the target, and the X axis is toward the golfer. The fairway frame is mainly used for describing the stop points of shots and for measuring AA, SPA, and CA.

frames of reference also called coordinate systems. See fairway frame and head frame. We used a number of other frames of reference, unnecessary for this description of the fundamentals.

FS [deg] face-shaft angle which a golfer may adjust to control hooks and slices (see Figure 25-4).

golfer P a representative golfer with CHD = 281 yards and HS = 114.1 mph on our reference T driver and with HCP = 0.

golfer A a representative golfer with CHD = 251 yards and HS = 100.7 mph on our reference T driver and with HCP = 10.

golfer B a representative golfer with CHD = 217 yards and HS = 87.2 mph on our reference T driver and with HCP = 20.

golfer C a representative golfer with CHD = 179 yards and HS = 73.8 mph on our reference T driver and with HCP = 27.5.

H [in] span, vertical distance from lowest to highest position of the clubhead for good shots.

HCP [ ] handicap.

head frame the right hand rectangular coordinate system with origin at the intersection of the sole line with an extension of the face surface, the Z axis coincides with the sole line, the shaft axis is in a plane parallel to the X-Y plane, and the X axis is toward the golfer and is below the shaft axis at the angle LIA. All

points of the head have positive Y values and the face center is in the Y-Z plane. The head frame moves with the head. The cg location, LA, FA, and LIA are measured in this frame. Figure 2-1 illustrates the head frame and dimensions of the cg location.

HS [mph] head speed, speed of the cg of the head just prior to impact.

HW [gm] head weight (mass), weight of the head without shaft.

ID [in] imprint diameter of a ball as it deforms against the club face, small for chip shots and progressively larger for strong hits.

iterate a trial and error process repeated many times with systematically improved inputs to find the combination which is as near as possible to the desired result.

LA [deg] loft angle. LA is measured in the head frame in a plane which is perpendicular to the face at the face center and to the X-Z plane; in this plane, it is the angle between a line parallel to the Y axis and the line which is tangent to the face at the face center.

LAE [deg] effective LA, somewhat different from LA because centrifugal force bends the shaft and at impact, and somewhat changes clubhead orientation; CA and wrist rotation also affect LAE.

launch direction see target direction.

LIA [deg] lie angle (more accurately, the acute angle in the head frame between the shaft axis and the X-Z plane, measured in a plane through the shaft axis parallel to the X-Y plane.)

Mb [lbf$*$in^2] moment of inertia of the ball.

MD [yd] maximum distance, the value of CHD with a particular shaft and grip with specific values of HW, CLG, and HS, with no golfer errors and when the head design is optimized for this condition.

ME [in] for putts, otherwise [yd] most probable error of stop points, taken to be the average error, measured from the stop point of an error-free center hit.

MEP [yd] same as ME but effects of POF hits are included.

mishits Is it a miss or a hit? Is it excremental? We use the more descriptive term, "off-center hits", specifically referring to hits not at the face center.

moment of inertia In golf writing, this is often called MOI as a single term. In fact, it takes 6 terms to describe the moment of inertia concept for a general body. One way to express this is a moment of inertia around each of 3 axes plus 3 products of inertia (which are sometimes zero). We will usually use moment of inertia to mean all 6 terms unless we state or imply a particular axis. A golf ball or any uniform sphere about its center has 3 equal moment of inertia terms and 3 zero product of inertia terms.

MRD [in] mean radial distance of putt stop points from the center of the hole, rather than from the aim point.

NCR [ ] coefficient of restitution for normal impulses.

P [lb/sq in] pressure to compress grass.

PD [ft] total distance of a putt.

Ph [ft] distance to center of hole for putting.

PHO [ ] putts needed to hole out.

POF hits partly off the face hits for those hits near the edge of the face for which more than 25% of the imprint area (of a center hit) would be off the face.

putter A an optimized design, our model 330.

putter R a popular design with low moments of inertia and cg which is much above optimum.

reference atmospheric conditions sea level altitude, 70 degrees F, no wind, and 20% relative humidity.

reference ball we used a ball which was popular a few years ago for all impact results, the Dunlop DDhII. In some other tests, we used a Spalding Top Flight Plus II as noted.

reference D driver imaginary ultimate design having 40 gram shaft, CLG = 48 inches, 180 gram head, and 20 gram grip, design optimized for each HS in question.

reference T driver a driver with 88 gram graphite shaft, CLG = 43 inches, HW = 200 grams, and 43.5 gram grip which we used in golfer tests and for frequent reference. Modern drivers usually give up to 5 yards greater CHD than this reference.

RR [in] roll radius, the radius of curvature of a club face in the up-down direction.

S [ft] Stimp reading which is the distance a ball rolls on grass after rolling freely down a specified ramp. We use a ramp with 2 parallel rails separated 3/4 inch, inclined above the horizontal at an angle of 19 degrees, and the release point is 10 inches above the horizontal. For hole zone research we used a similar device but with various release points and rails less separated.

SCR [ ] coefficient of restitution for shear impulses.

sole line the line of contact of the bottom of the club head with the X-Z plane of the head frame and is coincident with the Z axis.

SPA [deg] swing plane angle, the acute angle in the fairway frame between the normal to the swing plane and the Y axis.)

Sr [rps/sec] rate at which the ball is spinning.

Stimp reading see **S**.

TA [deg] target angle for putters, as defined in Figure 27-1.

target direction [deg] also called launch direction. It is the direction in which you want to launch the ball.

TBB [in] vertical distance, top of grass to bottom of ball.

UMD [yd] ultimate maximum CHD with reference D driver for any particular golfer class.

WA [deg] wrist angle which describes rotation of the club around a line connecting the grip butt and the head cg, zero when the face is square to the swing path at the bottom of the swing. It is a function of FS and the actual rotation of the golfer's wrist during the swing.

WAR [rps] rate of rotation around the WA axis at impact.

Wb [lb] weight of the ball.

X [yd, ft, or in] X coordinate, used in various coordinate systems.

Xcg [in] X location of the cg in the head frame, generally positive toward the heel (see Fig 2-1.)

Xstop [yd] X coordinate in the fairway frame where the ball stops.

Y [yds, ft, or in] Y coordinate, used in various coordinate systems, generally positive upward.

Ycg [in] Y location of the cg in the head frame, see Fig 2-1.

Ych [in] Y coordinate in the head frame of the ideal center for the hit pattern ellipse. For drivers, Ych = half the face depth (height) and for irons, Ych is different (see Technical Notes of Chapter 24.)

Z [yd, ft, or in] Z coordinate, used in various coordinate systems, generally positive in the target direction.

Zcg [in] Z location of the cg in the head frame, normally negative, see Fig 2-1.

Zstop [yards] Z coordinate in the fairway frame of where the ball stops.

ZBR [yd] bounce and roll distance for clubs other than putters, measured from where the ball hits down and the flight (carry) ends. See **PD** for putt distance.

REFERENCES

BOOKS

1. A. Cochran and J. Stobbs, *The Search for the Perfect Swing* (The Booklegger, Grass Valley CA, 1968).
2. C. Soley, *How Well Should You Putt?* (Soley Golf Bureau, San Jose, CA, 1977).
3. D. Pelz and N. Mastroni, *Putt Like the Pros* (Harper-Collins Publishers, New York, 1989).
4. A. J. Cochran (ed), *Science and Golf, Part 3* (E & FN Spon, London, 1990).
5. A. J. Cochran and M. R. Farrally (ed), *Science and Golf II*, Chapters 37-49 (E & FN Spon, London, 1994).
6. M. R. Farrally and A. J. Cochran (ed), *Science and Golf III*, Chapters 58 and 61-71 (Human Kinetics, Champaign, IL, 1999).
7. T. P. Jorgensen, *The Physics of Golf*, 2nd ed. (Springer-Verlag, New York, 1999).
8. S. F. Hoerner, *Fluid-Dynamic Drag*, pages 4-1 and 4-2 (published by the author, 1965).
9. D. Pelz and J. A. Frank, *Dave Pelz's Short Game Bible* (Broadway Books, New York, 1999).
10. S. H. Crandall and N. C. Dahl, *An Introduction to the Mechanics of Solids*, pages 306-314, (McGraw-Hill, 1959).

PAPERS

11. R. D. Milne and J. P. Davis, "The role of the shaft in the golf swing," *JBiomechanics, Vol l29, No 9*, p 975-983 (1992).
12. D. Pelz "A Simple scientific shaft test: steel versus graphite," p 284-269 in Reference 4 (1990).
13. G. P. Horwood, "Golf shafts—a technical perspective," p 245-258 in Reference 5 (1994).
14. F. D. Werner and R. C. Greig, "Golf putters and technology", *The Golfsmith Clubmaker*, published in 4 parts from April to December, 1992.
15. S. Aoyama, "A modern method of measuring aerodynamic lift and drag of golf balls," p 199-204 in Reference 4 (1990).
16. D. C. Hopkins and J. D. Patterson, "Bowling frames: paths of a bowling ball", *American Journal of Physics, Vol 45*, p 263-266 (1977).

INDEX

FRANK D. WERNER

Werner was born in Kansas in 1922. His education includes a B.S. degree in physics at Kansas State University, and M.S. and Ph.D. degrees in aerospace engineering at the University of Minnesota.

He first worked at The Johns Hopkins University's Applied Physics Laboratory, in Silver Spring, Maryland, on proximity fuse research for anti-aircraft artillery and radar improvements. From 1947 to 1956, he was a researcher in addition to his graduate work, and later became a member of the graduate faculty of the University of Minnesota, Department of Aerospace Mechanics. He spent much of his time there, researching aeronautical measuring instruments at U of M's Rosemount Aeronautical Laboratories.

In 1956 Werner became the president and principal founder of Rosemount Engineering Company in Minneapolis, Minnesota, now part of Fisher-Rosemount, a major division of Emerson Electric Company. Rosemount's early work involved research, development, and manufacture of a variety of measuring instruments for the aeronautical and space industry – still widely used in the aerospace industry. The firm has since become a leader in industrial instrumentation.

Werner moved to Jackson Hole, Wyoming in 1968 and founded Origin Inc, a small product development firm. One of Origin's several significant products was a windshield repair system now used world wide.

In 1970, Werner designed a putter as an interesting diversion, but he did not pursue it immediately. Sixteen years later, he and Dick Greig, vice president of Origin Inc and president of Tech Line Corp, took another look. This led to a highly refined and complex technical analysis of exactly what happens when a putter hits the golf ball. Next, they applied these analytical methods to the design of innovative drivers which are on the market today.

Werner's creative thinking has produced 80 patents.

While his hobbies have included golf, skiing, fishing and the mountains (he lives at the foot of the Teton Range), Werner says his greatest enjoyment is in problem solving. "Good solutions often require extensive creative thinking."

He and his wife, Alice, have 3 children and 8 grandchildren.

Richard C. Greig

Dick Greig was born in New Jersey in 1943, and raised in Minnesota from early childhood. His education includes B.S. and M.S. degrees in aerospace engineering from the University of Minnesota. He completed the course work and met the requirements for candidacy for the Ph.D. degree in the same field.

He has over 30 years of experience in research and development of technical products along with extensive managing and marketing experience at Origin Inc. Mathematical analysis and modeling has been a special interest. His major areas of study were fluid mechanics, kinetic theory of gases, applied mathematics and thermodynamics.

While at the university, Greig taught courses in fluid dynamics, dynamics, statics and deformable body mechanics at the undergraduate level and worked part time in research at the aeronautics lab.

During his university experience, he was introduced to computers and became fascinated with them. His initial exposure to programming in Fortran started him on an exciting and continuing self-taught course of study to model physical processes on computers. This process allows efficient design optimization. Although he writes most of his own code, he is conversant with and uses, where appropriate, many of the popular software programs available today.

Greig left the university to work for Origin Inc in 1971. He continues that association and is president of Tech Line Corp. He has applied his expertise to the thermal and economic modeling of domestic solar heating systems, economic trend analysis, and golf club design. He gained considerable experience in developing extrusion and injection molding and metal machining operations, and has a number of patents.

He and his wife, Judy, have three children.

THE BIGFACE 1 DRIVER

Here are photographs of the large face driver (BIGFACE 1) which we designed using the methods described in the book and which is referenced in several places. Many consider it to be strange looking, even ugly and some object to the loud sound of impact. Users consistently report that it gives perceptibly better accuracy ("fewer shots off the fairway"; it is "easier to hit"; it "improves confidence in the game"; "better distance"; and some even say "took 10 strokes off their handicap".) They learn to like its appearance and to disregard its sound. It was designed according to the methods outlined in this book for top performance, without regard for appearance and sound. It conforms to the USGA Rules of Golf.

TECH-LINE®

3975 S. Hwy 89, Jackson, WY 83001
307 733-4952 or 800 451-8858
www.techlinegolf.com

U.S. Patents 5,366,223, 5,380,010; others pending
© 2000 TECH-LINE CORP

ORDER FORM • *Fax, Phone or Mail*

By Fax: *Copy or remove this form, fill out, enter your Visa or MC card number, and sign. Fax to **307 739-1530**.*

By Phone: *Have your Visa or MC card number ready and phone **800 451-8858**.*

By Mail: *Fill out form, enter your Visa or MC card number and sign or include personal check (U.S. dollars only), and mail in envelope to Tech Line Corp, 3975 S Hwy 89, Jackson, WY 83001.*

TECH LINE CORP

❑ Please send ____ copies of this book for $34.95 ($5 S/H included) plus 6% tax for WY orders.

❑ Please send descriptive brochure on **BIGFACE 1** drivers.

❑ Please send descriptive brochure on **SCUFF-RAIL** putters.

Name ....

Address .... Email...

City.. State................................ Zip ....

Payment: ❑ Visa   ❑ MasterCard   ❑ Check

Card Number .... Exp. Date.......................

Print Name.. Signature ....

Visit our website at www.techlinegolf.com

ORDER FORM • *Fax, Phone or Mail*

By Fax: *Copy or remove this form, fill out, enter your Visa or MC card number, and sign. Fax to 307 739-1530.*

By Phone: *Have your Visa or MC card number ready and phone 800 451-8858.*

By Mail: *Fill out form, enter your Visa or MC card number and sign or include personal check (U.S. dollars only), and mail in envelope to Tech Line Corp, 3975 S Hwy 89, Jackson, WY 83001.*

TECH LINE CORP

❏ Please send ____ copies of this book for $34.95 ($5 S/H included) plus 6% tax for WY orders.

❏ Please send descriptive brochure on **BIGFACE 1** drivers.

❏ Please send descriptive brochure on **SCUFF-RAIL** putters.

Name ....

Address .... Email..

City.. State............................... Zip ....

Payment: ❏ Visa ❏ MasterCard ❏ Check

Card Number .... Exp. Date........................

Print Name.. Signature ....

Visit our website at www.techlinegolf.com